A Social Language Program

Author: Carolyn C. Wilson

Skill Area: Social Language
Developmental Age: 6-10

LinguiSystems®

LinguiSystems, Inc.
3100 4th Avenue
East Moline, IL 61244

1-800-776-4332

FAX: 1-800-577-4555
E-mail: service@linguisystems.com
Web: www.linguisystems.com

Printed in the U.S.A.
ISBN 1-55999-902-0

About the Author

Carolyn C. Wilson, M.S., CCC-SLP, is a speech-language pathologist in private practice in Fort Worth, Texas. She specializes in providing evaluations and intervention for children and adolescents who experience learning or social language problems related to language disorders. She has authored or co-authored a number of clinical books in these areas. Carolyn began her career in 1975 as a public school speech-language clinician and later served as instructor and clinical coordinator in speech-language pathology at Texas Christian University.

Dedication

Room 14 is dedicated with love to Jonathan who makes it all worthwhile and to my husband, Russell, whose encouragement makes it all possible.

Acknowledgment

I wish to thank Russell Wilson, M.Div., Sherrie Wilson, B.A., and Patsy Dickens, M.F.A., CCC-SLP for applying their various areas of professional expertise to reading and commenting on the *Room 14* manuscript.

Illustrator: Margaret Warner
Cover Design: Michael Paustian

Table of Contents

Introduction

Room 14 is a practical resource for building social language. *Room 14* will teach your students skills that reinforce social growth, personal happiness, and academic success.

Overview

Room 14 has an Instructor's Manual, an Activities Book, and a Picture Book. The Instructor's Manual contains a Social Skills Checklist, Social Skills Lessons, and an Appendix on relaxation techniques important for self-control. The Activities Book contains activity sheets to extend each lesson, a game sheet for each unit, and an answer key. The Picture Book contains pictures with questions that relate to each lesson.

The lessons are divided into five units focusing on successful language use in these important social areas:

Unit 1: Making and Keeping Friends
Unit 2: Fitting In at School
Unit 3: Handling Your Feelings
Unit 4: Using Self-Control
Unit 5: Being Responsible

Selecting Students

Room 14 is designed for both special and regular education students. It can be used for either remediation or prevention of social language problems.

Remediation: Social language instruction is an important part of educating students who interact inappropriately.

Prevention: Classrooms are effective places for social language instruction. All students benefit from learning social language skills and using them in their daily lives.

Whether used for remediation or prevention, the flexibility of *Room 14* makes it especially applicable to collaboration among various professionals whose goal is to help their students build social language skills.

Teaching the Lessons

Students learn social skills through a combination of approaches. That's why *Room 14* lessons offer a variety of teaching procedures. The lessons involve your students in important language activities, like speaking, listening, and using and understanding body language. In addition, they'll learn how to approach and respond to others.

Here's one approach for how to teach the social skills in *Room 14*:

- Discuss and model the skills.
- Let your students practice.
- Give helpful feedback.
- Reward the emerging skills.

There are various ways to use the lessons in *Room 14*, but here's a suggested way to use the components with the above approach.

Start with the Instructor's Manual and the Picture Book.

1. First, determine your students' social language needs with the Social Language Checklist found at the front of the Instructor's Manual. Then, choose lessons that will meet your students' needs.

2. Kick off your lesson with the high-interest activity found in the Preparation part of the lesson. Then, read aloud the Social Skills Story in the Instructor's Manual. Your students will identify with the *Room 14* characters who have social problems and social successes much like their own. The first picture for each lesson in the Picture Book illustrates the story.

3. After you read the story, use the Questions for Discussion section to talk about the skills in the story. Then, guide additional discussion with the last three lesson pictures in the Picture Book.

4. Help your students practice the skills with selected learning activities from the Social Skills Activities in the Instructor's Manual. Choose activities that will reinforce the individual needs of your students.

5. Use the Role-Play Activities in the Instructor's Manual to help your students practice the social skill. You may choose to take one of the role-play parts so students will learn from your model. The first role play is usually based on the Social Skills Story. Additional role plays give other practice situations.

6. Give positive reinforcement that will encourage your students' good feelings about what they learn through the role play by using the questions in the Role-Play Feedback section. Also, use the questions to teach your students to give their classmates helpful feedback that will help them look forward to more role-play fun.

Add the Activities Book.

7. Use the activity sheets as springboards for discussion and further practice. You might want your students to make their own social skills folder where they can place their completed activity sheets, as well as other social skills work.

8. Use the last activity sheet in each lesson to help your students decide on times and places to practice the skills they've learned. Refer back to the Instructor's Manual for examples of what your students might say.

9. Review the skills by using the Unit Game Sheets. The last activity sheet within each unit in the Activities Book is the Unit Game Sheet. You will need a marker for each player and a coin to play the games. Use the questions from the Picture Book as game questions. You may also want to guide a unit review with the Unit Game Sheets and questions from several lessons.

Use the Instructor's Manual again.

10. Wrap up your students' study by reading aloud the Visualization section. This way, you end your study by guiding your students, skill by skill, through a review of what they've learned.

Combine the *Room 14* lessons with your professional expertise and the lively participation of your students. The result will be hours of effective, language-learning experiences for your students!

Social Skills Checklist

This social skills checklist has a variety of uses. Here are a few suggestions:

- determining a student's strengths and areas for growth in social language
- developing a student's social language goals
- evaluating a student's social language progress

Each number on the checklist corresponds to a lesson in the *Room 14* Instructor's Manual. If the word *rarely* is marked, you may want to teach the lesson that corresponds to that number.

Making and Keeping Friends	often	sometimes	rarely
1. Introduces self to new people without being prompted.	❑	❑	❑
2. Initiates conversations rather than waiting for others to talk first.	❑	❑	❑
3. Ends conversations in a friendly way.	❑	❑	❑
4. Offers to share objects, ideas, and information appropriately.	❑	❑	❑
5. Volunteers to help others without taking over.	❑	❑	❑
6. Admits mistakes and sincerely says, "I'm sorry."	❑	❑	❑
7. Gives sincere compliments to peers and adults.	❑	❑	❑
8. Accepts compliments from peers and adults with a simple thank-you.	❑	❑	❑
Fitting In at School			
1. Demonstrates good classroom listening behavior with appropriate body language.	❑	❑	❑
2. Asks for help at appropriate times in the classroom.	❑	❑	❑
3. Says thank you to teachers and peers to show appreciation for help or considerate actions.	❑	❑	❑
4. Listens to and follows the teacher's directions.	❑	❑	❑
5. Asks questions to clarify statements or gain more information.	❑	❑	❑

6. Participates and stays on task during classroom discussions.	❑	❑	❑
7. Finishes and hands in schoolwork on time.	❑	❑	❑

Handling Your Feelings

1. Recognizes a variety of personal feelings.	❑	❑	❑
2. Uses feeling words to describe personal feelings.	❑	❑	❑
3. Controls anger with peers and adults.	❑	❑	❑
4. Handles fear constructively rather than becoming immobilized by it.	❑	❑	❑
5. Says positive things to self.	❑	❑	❑

Using Self-Control

1. Responds to strong feelings by cooling off before acting.	❑	❑	❑
2. Maintains control when teased by peers or adults.	❑	❑	❑
3. Asks permission before using another's belongings.	❑	❑	❑
4. Admits mistakes and accepts the consequences.	❑	❑	❑
5. Listens and responds calmly when wrongly accused.	❑	❑	❑

Being Responsible

1. Makes a complaint with confidence when things don't seem fair.	❑	❑	❑
2. Takes action to deal with hurt feelings when left out by friends.	❑	❑	❑
3. Practices good sportsmanship.	❑	❑	❑
4. Accepts no for an answer graciously and goes on to other activities.	❑	❑	❑
5. Firmly says no to unreasonable or harmful requests of others.	❑	❑	❑
6. Finds mutually acceptable solutions to conflicts with peers and adults.	❑	❑	❑

Making and Keeping Friends

"Who's in my class?" "Will I have any friends?" These are questions your students might ask when they enter a new classroom. Their questions have little to do with the teachers or the curriculum. Your students probably think more about being accepted by their peers.

Students in elementary grades are prime candidates for learning social language skills that will help them make and keep friends. They have reached a stage in their development in which friendships have become important to them. They're new, however, at friendship skills and have much to learn.

The lessons in Unit 1 will help your students initiate and maintain friendships through practice with the following social language skills:

Lesson 1: Introducing themselves to new people.

Lesson 2: Initiating conversations rather than waiting for others to talk first.

Lesson 3: Taking turns being the speaker and the listener during a conversation and bringing a conversation to a friendly end.

Lesson 4: Reaching out when friends have needs and offering to share.

Lesson 5: Offering to help a friend without being bossy or pushy.

Lesson 6: Admitting mistakes and sincerely saying, "I'm sorry."

Lesson 7: Praising a friend for doing something well.

Lesson 8: Accepting a compliment with a friendly thank-you.

Lesson 1: Introducing Yourself

Skills

A. Ask yourself, "Do I want to meet this person?"

B. Walk up to the person you want to meet.

C. Smile and say hello.

D. Tell your new friend your name.

E. Listen to your new friend's name.

Materials

Activities Book:
pages 5 through 7

Picture Book:
pages 6 through 13

Introduction

Your students must be able to introduce themselves in order to make new friends. They need to be able to offer greetings, give information, and ask for information. Many students may want to make friends, yet they resort to behavior that leads to rejection because they're unable to use these simple skills.

Students in the early elementary grades are prime candidates for learning basic social skills that will enable them to make friends. They have reached a stage in their development when friendships are or have become important to them. Still, they're new at making and keeping friends. They need to learn social skills that enable them to work and play cooperatively with other students.

Goals

In this lesson, your students will learn to introduce themselves. The activities will help your students

- give information
- ask for information
- offer greetings
- learn that not every person should be their friend
- learn to ask themselves, "Do I want to introduce myself to this person?"

Preparation

Create a friendly atmosphere to give your students courage to initiate new relationships. Tell your students about a friendship you enjoy because you walked up and introduced yourself to someone. Be honest and tell them that introducing yourself to a person can be scary. But making a new friend is worth the risk.

Ask your students, "What is a friend?" Say, "Friends understand you. You don't have to pretend with friends. You can be yourself. Friends won't make fun of you."

Say, "Making friends is important. Now, you might make a friend who will still be your friend when you're grown." Point out that there are new friends waiting for them. That's why it's important for your students to learn to introduce themselves.

Social Skills Story

Use page 6 in the Picture Book with this story. Tell your students that meeting new friends can be both exciting and scary. Ask, "How do you feel when you're the new person in a group? How do you feel when someone walks up to you and introduces himself? Mrs. Sahwani introduced herself to Marci on Marci's first day of school. Listen to this story."

Marci sighed as she packed her new backpack. She and her mother had moved to a new town so her mother could take a better job. For Marci, the move meant getting used to a new neighborhood, new teachers, and new classmates.

"Are you ready, Marci?" called her mom.

Marci checked her backpack to see if she'd forgotten anything. "I guess so," said Marci.

During the ride to school, Marci's mom talked about the tall trees in their new town. Marci was quiet. She didn't care about the tall trees. She liked her old town, old school, and old friends. "What will my new teacher be like? Will I have any friends?" she wondered.

Then, Marci's mom slowed to a stop in the school parking lot. "Changes are hard," she said. "But changes can be adventures. You never know what new friends you're going to meet."

"That's what you think," thought Marci. "Nobody will like me. They'll laugh at my freckles. They always do."

At the classroom door, Marci's mom gave Marci a hug and said good-bye.

Then, a smiling teacher walked up to Marci and said, "Good morning. My name is Mrs. Sahwani. Welcome to Room 14. What's your name?"

Marci smiled, too, and she felt a little better. "It's Marci Valentino," said Marci.

"Hello, Marci," said her new teacher. Then, she handed Marci a paper cutout of an orange giraffe. "This giraffe will help you find a friend," she said. "Someone else has an orange giraffe, too. Find that friend and introduce yourself. That person will be your partner in a game we'll play later."

Marci looked around the room. Four or five students were putting their books away. Each one carried a paper animal. Marci saw a boy holding an orange giraffe. The boy walked up to her and introduced himself.

Marci noticed that the boy had freckles, too. "I think I have a new friend," Marci thought.

Questions for Discussion

Say, "Let's think of some skills to remember when you're introducing yourself to a new friend." Write the skills on the chalkboard or a flip chart as your students respond.

1. What was Marci's problem?

   She was afraid she wouldn't have any friends.

2. Who introduced themselves to Marci? How did the teacher introduce herself?

   Mrs. Sahwani and a boy. The teacher said, "Good morning" and she told Marci her name.

3. Why do you think Mrs. Sahwani wanted to meet Marci?

   She was new at school. (Write **Ask yourself, "Do I want to meet this person?"***)*

4. Tell why you might want to meet someone.

   Answers will vary.

5. What did Mrs. Sahwani do when she wanted to meet Marci?

   She walked up to her. (Write **Walk up to the person you want to meet.***)*

6. How did Marci feel when her new teacher smiled and said good morning?

   She felt better. (Write **Smile and say hello.***)*

7. How did Mrs. Sahwani find out Marci's name?

   Mrs. Sahwani asked Marci. (Write **Tell your new friend your name.***)*

8. Marci told Mrs. Sahwani her name. What would you do if you wanted to remember someone's name?

   Listen to the person when she tells you her name. (Write **Listen to your new friend's name.***)*

Social Skills Activities

Skill A

Ask Yourself, "Do I Want to Meet This Person?"

1. Encourage your students to discuss their choice of friends and why they have them as friends. Then, give each student a sheet of paper, a pencil, and some markers. Have your students fold the paper into thirds. Then, have them draw one friend in each area. Help your students write a sentence below each picture to tell why the person was a good person to meet.

2. Talk about how people become friends. Point out that someone has to start a new friendship by being friendly. Introducing yourself to a new person is a way to be friendly. Ask, "What is a friend? What does a friend do?" Have your students think of friends they've already made while they complete these sentences:

   A friend is someone who . . .

   I like my friend because . . .

   My friend deserves a medal for . . .

   My friend doesn't . . .

   I can trust my friend because . . .

   At school, my friend and I . . .

3. Have your students raise their hands if it would be all right to meet the following people:

a boy your age climbing the jungle gym by himself *yes*

an adult working on your neighbor's roof *no*

a stranger in a car asking you if you want a ride home *no*

a girl your age playing basketball alone at the park *yes*

Skill B

Walk Up to the Person You Want to Meet

1. Use puppets to help your students develop the courage to walk up to a person they'd like to meet. Provide hand puppets or have your students make simple puppets. Then, have your students practice walking one puppet across the desk toward the other puppet and saying "Hi, my name is . . . . What's your name?"

2. Have your students brainstorm good times and places to meet new friends. Ask, "Which time would be better for introducing yourself to a new person, when the person is by herself, or when she's playing a game with a group? Usually, it helps to approach a new person when she's not busy with other people."

3. Standing an appropriate distance from a person is important. Some students don't know how far to stand from another person. Put two long strips of tape on the floor about an arm's length away from each other. Divide your students into pairs. Have one student in each pair stand on a piece of tape. Have each student in each pair introduce himself to the other.

   Then, have your students stand inside the tape as they talk to each other. Discuss how uncomfortable they feel being so close.

Skill C

Smile and Say Hello

1. Talk about friendly body language. Say, "To make a new friend, you must be friendly." Ask, "What can you do to show that you're friendly? Smiling and saying hi are good ways to show you're friendly."

   Give your students hand mirrors. Have your students practice various expressions as you name the expressions. Point out the differences between friendly expressions and other expressions, like sad, angry, proud, disgusted, frightened, and withdrawn.

2. Encourage friendly behavior in your students by pointing it out. "Michael, I like your smile. You look so friendly." "Jill, you looked so friendly when you were helping Miguel with the work he missed."

Skill D

Tell Your New Friend Your Name

1. Talk about the importance of good eye contact and clear speech. Point out that these things help someone new remember your students' names. Ask, "Why is it important to tell a new friend your name?" Give each student a turn to practice saying, "My name is . . . ." Emphasize the importance of using good eye contact when they say their names.

Skill E

Listen to Your New Friend's Name

1. Bring a book of names and their meanings to school. Help your students look up the meanings of their own names and names of friends and family members.

2. Play "Name Game" to stress the importance of names and give an opportunity for new friends to learn more about each other. Give each student a sheet of construction paper, some markers, and some crayons. Have each student spell her name down the left side of the paper. Beside each letter, help her write a word or phrase beginning with the letter that describes herself. Use Chee's name as an example:

   C cute
   H healthy
   E energetic
   E eats broccoli

Additional Activities

Role-Playing

Review the story in this lesson. Then, select one or both of the following role-play activities.

Choose volunteers to play Mark and Marci. Pretend that Marci is new at school and Mark introduces himself to her. Mark has the giraffe that matches Marci's. Remind the students playing Mark and Marci to use good eye contact, smile, be friendly, stand an arm's length away, and say their names.

Choose volunteers to play Bonnie and a new girl named Rachel. Pretend Rachel moved in down the street from Bonnie. She looks friendly and Bonnie wants a new friend. One day when they're outside, Bonnie goes up and introduces herself. The girl says her name is Rachel. Remind the students playing Rachel and Bonnie to use good eye contact, smile, be friendly, stand an arm's length away, and say their names.

Role-Play Feedback

Encourage the rest of your students to give helpful feedback to the role-play volunteers. Use the following questions:

> What did you like about each character's part?
>
> What did Mark do that was friendly? Explain.
>
> What did Bonnie do that was friendly? Explain.
>
> Did Bonnie include all the skills for introducing herself?
>
> How could these role plays be different?

Expanding Learning

Use pages 5 and 6 in the Activities Book to help your students remember what to say when they introduce themselves. Discuss why they might want to meet a person and become friends.

Use pages 6 through 13 in the Picture Book to help your students learn more about

- deciding who to introduce themselves to
- introducing themselves to a parent's friend
- introducing themselves to a peer with a disability
- not introducing themselves to strangers

Use page 7 in the Activities Book to help your students review the skills learned for introducing themselves. Have your students suggest when and how to review the skills. For example, a student may say

> "I will ask myself if I want to meet the girl jumping rope."
>
> "I will walk up to her."

"I will say hello."

"I will say, 'My name is Simone.' "

"I will listen for her name."

Visualization

Have your students get in comfortable positions to relax. Then say, "Close your eyes and imagine introducing yourself to a new friend.

"A new student comes to your class. He looks friendly, and he likes to skateboard just like you do. During recess you see the new student standing by himself, so you walk over to him. You smile and say hi. You tell him your name. He tells you his name. You say, 'I know where we can find some cool rocks on the playground, want to see?' Your new friend says, 'Yes, that'll be fun!' You're glad to have a new friend."

Lesson 2: Starting a Conversation

Skills

A. Choose a good time and place to talk.

B. Decide what to talk about.

C. Get the person's attention.

D. Start talking in a friendly way.

Materials

Activities Book:
pages 8 through 10

Picture Book:
pages 14 through 21

Introduction

Some students have a difficult time starting a conversation, so they often only speak when spoken to. These students miss out on many opportunities for developing friendships.

Other students will try to begin conversations with their friends, but they don't know how to greet their friends appropriately. Some students start every conversation the same way. Other students interrupt ongoing conversations. When students inappropriately start or interrupt conversations, others may ignore them, or may even feel frightened, confused, or angry.

The ability to start conversations effectively increases the chances that your students will be accepted by their peers. Knowing how to initiate conversations smoothly will boost your students' confidence and will increase their acceptance in their schools, homes, and communities.

Goals

In this lesson, your students will improve skills for initiating conversations. The activities will help your students

- start conversations at times and places that won't disturb others
- choose a friendly topic to discuss
- avoid plunging into a conversation until they get their friends' attention

Preparation

Observe your students' attempts to begin conversations during group projects, recess, or lunchtime. Do any of them repeatedly receive a cold shoulder when they try to initiate conversations? Do peers mock them when they attempt to enter conversations? If so, what seems to be causing their difficulty? Are they interrupting conversations or activities? Do they begin conversations in midstream or before they've gained the other person's attention? Do any of your students avoid initiating conversations altogether?

Talk about the meanings of the words *conversation* and *greeting*. Ask your students what a conversation is. Then, give your students the following definition. A conversation happens when at least two people

- talk together about a subject
- take turns being the speaker and the listener

- share and try to understand the other's ideas

Next, ask your students what they would say to someone who walked in the door. Explain that words, like *hi*, *hello*, and *good morning* are called *greetings*. Greetings are the friendly words you say to a person when you first meet. If you know the person, you may use his name in the greeting by saying, "Hi, Charlie!" or "Hello, Mr. Parrish."

Tell your older students that greetings may be informal or formal. *Informal greetings*, like "Hi, Dad," are used with people they know well. *Formal greetings*, such as "Hello, Mr. Hightower," are used with adults or people they don't know well. Ask your students to list informal and formal greetings they use.

Social Skills Story

Use page 14 in the Picture Book with this story. Discuss the importance of gaining a listener's attention with a greeting and good eye contact before beginning a conversation. Ask, "Why is it important to smile and say hi before you start a conversation with someone?" Say, "Jonathan needed to learn how to start a conversation. Listen to this story."

Mrs. Sahwani was writing busily at her desk when Jonathan entered the classroom.

"Know what?" asked Jonathan. Mrs. Sahwani jumped when she heard Jonathan's voice.

Jonathan said, "I brought my harmonica to school today. I'm taking it to music class 'cause Mr. Lenski said it's okay."

Mrs. Sahwani said, "Well, Jonathan, that's certainly nice, but I would've liked it better if you said hello when you came into the room. You frightened me."

"I'll try to remember, Mrs. Sahwani," said Jonathan.

Across the room, Mark was telling José about his new 3-D backpack. Jonathan walked across the room to join the guys.

"Know what?" asked Jonathan again. "I brought my harmonica to . . . "

"Watch the people move on my backpack when I move!" Mark interrupted. He and José walked across the room making the backpack move. Jonathan watched them.

"Why doesn't anyone want to hear about my harmonica?" Jonathan wondered.

Just then Marci came in and headed straight for Mrs. Sahwani.

"Know what, Marci?" Jonathan asked loudly, trying to get Marci's attention as she zoomed past. "My dad let me bring my harmonica to school. Just wait 'til you hear my harmonica, Marci." But Marci didn't hear Jonathan at all. She was worried about a lost homework paper and wanted to tell Mrs. Sahwani her problem.

Questions for Discussion

Say, "Let's think of skills Jonathan can follow next time to help him start a conversation better." Write the skills on the chalkboard or a flip chart as your students respond.

1. How did Jonathan feel when no one listened to him?

   sad, frustrated

2. True or false? Jonathan chose good times to talk.

   false (Write **Choose a good time and place to talk.***)*

3. What was wrong with the times Jonathan chose to talk with Mrs. Sahwani and José?

   Mrs. Sahwani was busy at her desk. José and Mark were already talking about something else.

4. Had Jonathan decided on a topic to talk about? If so, what?

   Yes. He wanted to talk about his harmonica.

5. Why is it important to choose a topic to talk about?

   so you have something to talk about, so you can keep a conversation going (Write **Decide what to talk about.***)*

6. Jonathan always said the same words to get another person's attention. Can you think of a better way to get another person's attention?

   Use greetings and use people's names, like "Hello, Mrs. Sahwani." (Write **Get the person's attention.***)*

7. Another way to be sure you have your friend's attention is to use good eye contact. How can you tell when you have good eye contact with your friend?

   Your eyes meet; you're looking at each other.

8. What ways can you show a friendly attitude when you start a conversation?

   Smile and say something friendly, like "Are you going to the library, too? Would you like to walk with me?" Also, give your friend a chance to talk. (Write **Start talking in a friendly way.***)*

Social Skills Activities

Skill A

Choose a Good Time and Place to Talk

1. Time: Say, "Show me thumbs-up when the time I describe would be a good time for a conversation with your friend. Show thumbs-down when the time is a poor one."

   You sit down next to your friend in the library. *down*

   Your friend is walking home from school. You're going the same way. *up*

   Your friend is talking to his mom. *down*

   You and your friend are standing next to each other at recess. *up*

   A new student is playing by herself at recess. *up*

   Your friend is sitting alone on the steps to his apartment. *up*

   Your best friend is listening to tapes. *down*

2. Place: Say, "Try to begin a conversation in a place that won't disturb others. What's wrong with starting a conversation in these places?"

   the classroom during math

   a movie theater

your house when your family is watching a video

a school auditorium during a program

a bedroom when someone is sleeping

What other places or times wouldn't be right for starting a conversation?

Skill B

Decide What to Talk About

1. Tell your students they need a topic to talk about when they start a conversation. A good topic to start with is one their friends are interested in. They could ask their friends about themselves and their activities.

   Some questions are better than others. Give your students ideas for topics to talk about.

   Use the following questions to help students distinguish between good and poor topics.

   Have your students stand up when they hear a question that would present a good topic to discuss and sit down when they hear a question that wouldn't be a good topic to discuss.

   Guess what happened yesterday? *up*

   What sports do you like? *up*

   Why do you have a bumpy nose? *down*

   Why do you wear your hair like that? *down*

   Would you like to play volleyball with me? *up*

   Do you like music? *up*

   How much money does your father make? *down*

   How's your mom after her surgery? *up*

   Are you as rich as the family says, Aunt Pauline? *down*

   Do you have any pets? What kind? *up*

   Did you see that Walt Disney movie last night? *up*

   What books do you like to read? *up*

   Why are your teeth so crooked? *down*

2. Point out that many adults enjoy talking with children. There are many questions children can ask to start a conversation with adults.

   Choose student volunteers to role-play the following questions with you or another adult. Then, the volunteers should continue the conversations.

   Did you have a nice day, Aunt Maria?

   What was your first pet, Grandpa?

   What did you do to earn money when you were a kid, Mom?

   Did you like school when you were a kid, Dad?

   Are we going anywhere this weekend, Grandma?

Skill C

Get the Person's Attention

1. Practice appropriate greetings with puppets. First, review the story in this lesson in which Jonathan startled Mrs. Sahwani by walking in and saying "Know what?" when she was busy at her desk. Point out that other people expect to hear a greeting and their name to get their attention. Review the point that saying "Know what?" doesn't say who a person wants to talk to, and it might not get a particular person's attention.

   Then, provide simple puppets and have your students dramatize getting a listener's attention. Have your students role-play a puppet going to another puppet, saying hi and the puppet's name, establishing good eye contact, and saying something friendly.

2. Teach your students that greetings between friends are different from greetings your students would use with an adult. Ask them to tell some greetings they use with their friends. Ask, "How are those greetings different from the greetings you use with your teachers and other adults?"

   Then say, "Pretend your name is Jasper Goodman and you're eight years old. We'll also pretend I'm your age and I want to start a conversation with you. Which greetings would you like to hear?"

   "Hi, Jasper!"

   "Hey, man."

   "Hello, Jasper."

   "Good morning, Mr. Goodman."

   "Come here."

Skill D

Start Talking in a Friendly Way

1. Use the following tips to guide a discussion about how to make friendly conversation, or small talk. After the discussion, encourage students to make posters about friendly conversation.

   Be pleasant. Smile and say hello in a friendly way.

   Be interested. Ask a question about the other person. Take time to get to know your friend better.

   Be thoughtful. Choose a topic you both have in common, such as sports, music, or school.

   Be a good listener. Take turns talking. The more you listen, the better you'll get to know your friend.

Additional Activities

Role-Playing

Review the story in this lesson. Then, select one or more of the following role-play activities.

Choose volunteers to play Jonathan and Mrs. Sahwani. Pretend Jonathan tells Mrs. Sahwani about his harmonica. Remind the person playing Jonathan to use a greeting.

Choose volunteers to play Jonathan, José, and Mark. Pretend that Jonathan wants to talk to José and Mark when he gets to Room 14. Remind the person playing Jonathan to choose a good time for talking.

Choose volunteers to play Jonathan and José. Pretend Jonathan brought a harmonica to music class and José has a violin. The students have a few minutes to talk before Mr. Lenski begins class. Remind the student playing Jonathan to use a greeting.

Choose volunteers to play Mark and Chee. Pretend Mark has gone to the dentist with his dad. While he is waiting, he sees Chee. Mark wants to start a conversation with Chee. Show how Mark decides on a topic to talk about and starts a conversation.

Role-Play Feedback

Encourage the rest of your students to give helpful feedback to the role-play volunteers. Use the following questions:

What did you like about each character's part?

What skills did Jonathan use for starting a conversation?

Did Mark include all the skills for starting a conversation? How could you tell?

How could these role plays be different?

Expanding Learning

Use pages 8 and 9 in the Activities Book to help your students

- learn to start conversations with friendly comments
- choose good times and places for their conversations

Use pages 14 through 21 in the Picture Book to help your students improve skills in starting conversations by

- learning appropriate greetings for starting conversations
- getting their listeners' attention before beginning conversations
- choosing good times and places to talk, and saying friendly things as they start conversations

Use page 10 in the Activities Book to help your students review the skills learned for starting conversations. Have your students suggest when and how they can practice these skills. For example, they might say

"A good time to talk is during recess."

"I will talk about the monkey bars."

"I will get the person's attention by saying hello."

"I will say, 'Do you want to play on the monkey bars?' "

Visualization

Have your students get in comfortable positions to relax. Then say, "Imagine yourself starting a conversation with your friend. It's a good time for a conversation because your friend isn't busy and your conversation won't disturb anyone.

"You walk up to your friend, smile, and say hi in a friendly way. Your friend looks up, your eyes meet, and he says hi to you. He seems glad to see you. So, you think of something friendly to say, such as 'Did you watch that movie last night?' He says, 'No, was it good?' You tell him about one of the best parts.

"Then, you listen while he talks. You're having a good time talking with your friend. You're glad you know how to start a friendly conversation."

Lesson 3: Having and Ending a Conversation

Skills

A. Take turns talking and listening.

B. Decide if it's time to finish the conversation.

C. End the conversation in a friendly way.

Materials

Activities Book:
pages 11 through 13

Picture Book:
pages 22 through 29

Introduction

Some students have difficulty taking turns speaking and listening. They may hog the conversation or take the role of a passive listener. Some students may interrupt a speaker or leave without bringing a conversation to an end. Others may not notice when it's time to end a conversation.

Communication skills aren't complete until students have learned to maintain and end conversations. These are high-level skills, but they're skills your students have been working on for several years. You can make their learning task easier.

Goals

In this lesson, your students will learn to maintain and end conversations in friendly ways. These skills are important for making and keeping friends. The activities in this lesson will teach your students to

- take turns being the speaker and listener
- give friendly endings to their conversations
- learn when to end a conversation

Preparation

Observe your students' conversations during recess, group projects, or lunchtime. Which students are the talkers? Which are the listeners? Are any of them the same students? Which students take turns talking and listening?

What do your students do to bring their conversations to a close? Do your students simply walk away or do they make farewell comments that end conversations, such as "Well, I've got to go now. It was nice talking to you"?

Remind your students that partners in a conversation take turns talking and listening. Ask, "What other times do you take turns?" Suggest that taking turns in conversation is like taking turns while playing games.

Tell your students that listening is just as important to a conversation as talking is. Compare the roles of listener and talker to the roles of catcher and pitcher in baseball. Good catching (listening) and good pitching (talking) are both important to a game of conversation.

Say, "A conversation has three parts: a beginning, a middle, and an end. Do you remember what the beginning of a conversation can be called?" Your students are right if they say a greeting.

Then, point out that the end of a conversation can be called the farewell.

Ask your students to name ways to say farewell. "Good-bye," "See you later," and "See you around" are a few. Say, "People say their farewells in different ways, but everyone has a way to end conversations." If your students know some farewells in other languages, talk about them. "Adios," "Adieu," "Au revoir," and "Auf Wiedersehen" are a few. Point out that every language has ways to end conversations.

Social Skills Story

Use page 22 in the Picture Book with this story. Ask, "Why is it important to give the listener a friendly comment to let him know you need to end the conversation?" *It closes your conversation and helps both of you look forward to your next conversation.*

Say, "Bonnie and Chee enjoyed their conversation at school one day, but when it was time to finish talking, they didn't know what to say. Listen to this story."

One morning, Mrs. Sahwani's class was spending recess indoors because it was raining. Bonnie decided to spend her free time drawing. She was drawing a picture of a big gray and red bus when Chee walked up.

"Hi, Bonnie," said Chee. "I like that bus you're drawing."

Bonnie looked up and smiled. "Hi, Chee," she said. "Thanks. I'm riding a bus like this to visit my cousin. She has a new baby."

"By yourself? Wow!" said Chee. Her eyes were wide.

Bonnie laughed. "No, I'm going with Aunt Dean and my little sister Nikia. Then, Mom and Dad and my brother and my other cousin are coming later."

"You sure have a lot of people in your family, Bonnie," said Chee.

Bonnie's eyebrows raised, "Eight right now 'cause Aunt Dean, my cousin Janine, and Grandma are living with us."

"Do you like having a big family?" Chee asked.

Bonnie laid down her red crayon. "Well, most of the time it's fun. But sometimes I'd like to have a room of my own. Now, I have to share with Nikia. How many people are in your family, Chee?"

Chee tilted her head. "My sister, my grandmother and grandfather Kaying, and me. That's four," she said. "We have cousins too, but they live a long way from here."

Both girls heard Mrs. Sahwani say, "It's time to put away your free-time activities."

The girls just stopped talking. Then, Chee headed toward her desk.

Questions for Discussion

Say, "Bonnie and Chee had a conversation that had a beginning and a middle. Which part did they leave out? Let's talk about their conversation and think of skills to help them with their next conversation." Write the skills on the chalkboard or a flip chart as your students respond.

1. Did Bonnie and Chee take turns talking and listening?

   Yes. (Write **Take turns talking and listening.***)*

2. How could you tell?

   First, Chee said something to Bonnie and Bonnie said something to Chee. Then, Chee asked a question. Bonnie answered the question and asked Chee a question.

3. What happened to make Chee and Bonnie end their conversation?

   Free time was over. (Write **Decide if it's time to finish the conversation.***)*

4. Name some things that might make you have to end your own conversations.

   Answers will vary.

5. How did Bonnie and Chee end their conversation?

   They just stopped talking. Chee turned and left.

6. Pretend to be Bonnie and Chee. Show one way you could end your conversation.

   You could smile and say, "Well, I've got to get back to my desk." You could reply, "Bye. See you at lunch." (Write **End the conversation in a friendly way.***)*

Social Skills Activities

Skill A
Take Turns Talking and Listening

1. Play "Ball of String" with students who tend to monopolize conversations. This game will help these students give other people turns to talk. Have two students sit on the floor facing each other. Provide a ball of string or yarn, and a topic to discuss. The student holding the ball of string is the speaker and the other student is the listener.

   Give the ball of string to the student who begins the conversation. When he finishes his first statement, he tosses the string to his partner. She adds comments and tosses it back to the first speaker, who says something else and tosses it back, and so on through five or six exchanges. Encourage students to stay on topic.

2. Play "Interview" to help your shyest students learn to take a conversational turn. Your students may play either the part of interviewer or interviewee.

   Have the interviewer try to find out about

   all the houses his friend has lived in

   foods and snacks his friend enjoys most

   some happy memories about holidays

   ways his friend likes to spend free time

   what his friend wants to grow up to be

   Encourage the student being interviewed to follow these rules:

   Tell all you can about each question.

   Stick to the subject of the question.

   Ask a question when you don't understand.

Skill B

Decide if It's Time to Finish the Conversation

1. Ask a student to talk to you. Next, model the nonverbal actions below. Then, have the other students tell whether the cues indicate you want to continue or end the conversation.

   smile and look interested *continue*

   look at your watch *end*

   look away *end*

   eye contact with questioning expression *continue*

   surprised expression *continue*

   yawn *end*

2. Point out that many things can happen to make you have to end a conversation. Have a brainstorming session in which your students name all the situations they can think of. Say, "Pretend you and your friend are having a conversation. Something happens to make you end it. What could it be?"

   A parent gives you a chore; grandma arrives for a visit; recess is over; you go into the library or another place where talking isn't permitted; the bus comes; your dad arrives to pick you up; you start feeling sick; answers will vary.

Skill C

End the Conversation in a Friendly Way

1. Ask, "Why is it important to make sure the other person says all he wants to say before you end a conversation?" Tell your students an exception could be when an emergency interrupts a conversation. When that happens, your students can offer a sincere apology, such as "I'm sorry I can't finish talking right now. Maybe we can finish our conversation another time."

2. Ask, "Why should you smile and say something friendly when you end a conversation?" Point out that friendly behavior helps your students be more well-liked. It also helps the other person look forward to another conversation with them. It lets both partners know the conversation is over.

3. Many students don't know what to say to end conversations. Help them by using a script. Divide your students into pairs to role-play. Encourage them to smile in a friendly way as they say the words.

   First student: Oh, my Mom's calling. I enjoyed talking.

   Second student: Me, too. I'll see you later.

   First student: Here's my dad. I've got to run.

   Second student: Bye. See you tomorrow.

   First student: I'd like to talk more, but my tooth is hurting. I'll talk to you tomorrow. Bye.

   Second student: I hope you feel better soon. Bye.

   First student: I need to finish my homework now. Let's talk on the phone later. Bye for now.

   Second student: Okay. I'll call you tonight. Bye.

   First student (on bus): Oh, here's my house. It was fun talking. See you again Monday.

   Second student: Bye. Have fun this weekend.

Additional Activities

Role-Playing

Review the story in this lesson. Then, select one or more of the following role-play activities.

Choose volunteers to play Chee and Bonnie. Pretend that Chee and Bonnie are having a conversation during inside recess. Mrs. Sahwani told them to go back to their seats. Remind the students playing Chee and Bonnie to use the skills for ending a conversation.

Choose volunteers to play Mark and Jonathan. Pretend Mark is planting seeds in a flowerpot for a science project. Jonathan walks over to Mark holding his seeds and a flowerpot. He greets Mark and they talk about how to plant their seeds. Just as they're finishing their planting, a bell rings for lunchtime. Remind the students to use the skills for starting, having, and ending conversations.

Choose volunteers to play Mrs. Sahwani and José. Pretend Mrs. Sahwani is standing near the classroom door waiting for her students to hang up their coats. José walks up to Mrs. Sahwani. José greets Mrs. Sahwani and they talk about their weekends. The bell rings. It's time for the students to be in their desks. Remind the students to use the skills for starting, having, and ending conversations.

Role-Play Feedback

Encourage the rest of your students to give helpful feedback to the role-play volunteers. Use the following questions:

What did you like about each character's part?

How did Chee and Bonnie end their conversation?

Did the students playing Mark and Jonathan take turns talking? How could you tell?

How did Mrs. Sahwani and José end their conversation?

How could these role plays be different?

Expanding Learning

Use pages 11 and 12 in the Activities Book to help your students

- improve their conversations by taking turns being the speaker and listener
- close their conversations in friendly ways

Use pages 22 through 29 in the Picture Book to help your students improve their conversations by

- knowing that a conversation needs a friendly ending
- bringing a conversation to a quick, but friendly close when your students don't feel like talking
- reviewing the three parts of a good conversation–beginning, middle, and end
- closing a telephone conversation appropriately

Use page 13 in the Activities Book to help your students review skills for having conversations and ending them in friendly ways. Have your students suggest when and how they can practice. For example, a student may say

"I will take turns talking and listening to my friend, Marci, at recess."

"I will talk and listen to Marci until it's time to go inside."

"I will say, 'It's time to go in. I'll talk to you later.' "

Visualization

Have your students get in comfortable positions to relax. Then say, "Close your eyes and imagine yourself having a friendly conversation. It has a greeting, a middle, and a farewell.

"You see a friend sitting on a bench in front of the school waiting for a ride home. You walk up, smile, and say hi in a friendly way. Your friend smiles, too, so you sit on the bench about an arm's distance away. You talk about the art project you've both been working on. You take turns being the speaker and the listener.

"Then, you see your friend's dad drive up, so you know it's time to end your conversation. You say, 'It was fun talking to you. See you later.' Your friend smiles, and tells you 'Good-bye. See you tomorrow!' You feel glad you know how to have and end a conversation with your friend."

Lesson 4: Caring and Sharing

Skills

A. Decide if you want to share.

B. Share when someone has a need, not later.

C. Go to the person and offer to share.

D. Share in a friendly way.

Materials

Activities Book:
pages 14 through 17

Picture Book:
pages 30 through 37

Introduction

Very young children often don't like to share. They're not developmentally able to think of others' needs. By the time they're five or six, however, children can play together cooperatively, sharing toys and ideas.

Sharing is a reaching-out behavior associated with positive actions like participating, joining in, and enjoying things with others. Sharing is one of the keys to the survival and growth of any human relationship. Students must learn to share to make and keep friends.

Goals

In this lesson, your students will learn to share with others. The activities will help your students

- learn the importance of sharing by taking the perspective of others
- think about how it feels to be left out
- choose to share their possessions, time, or thoughts with others

Preparation

Praise your students for sharing. Use the opportunity when you notice a student offer her partner a favorite pencil by comments like, "Jamalea, you shared your pencil. That's a good way to make a friend."

Ask a few students to tell about times when they shared with a friend. Then, ask these questions to guide a discussion: "How do you feel when you share? How do you feel when someone shares with you? How do you feel when someone doesn't share with you? Why is it important to share?"

Let your students help you make a bulletin board. Use this heading: A Friend is Someone Who Shares. Then, give each student one large cutout of a "talk bubble," similar to those in cartoons. Help your students write their thoughts about sharing, like "Sharing is . . . " and "I share because . . . ."

Say, "True or false? A student who never shares will end up with very few friends." Ask your students to explain their answers.

Social Skills Story

Use page 30 in the Picture Book with this story. Focus on sharing as a good way to make friends. Ask, "What are some of your favorite toys? Do you share those toys with friends?" Then say, "The time to share with friends is when they need or would enjoy using our things, not when they're busy doing other things. Bonnie made a friend because she shared a toy one day when Marci needed one. Listen to this story."

Bonnie sat at her desk and plopped a soft, cuddly teddy bear beside her. "There, Grayson," she told the bear, "you sit here while I put my books on my desk."

It was a special day in Room 14. The students in Mrs. Sahwani's class were bringing their favorite stuffed bears or other animals to school.

Bonnie's friends came to class, each carrying a stuffed animal. Jonathan had a big, fluffy bear with one ear missing, and Mark's little, black bear was dressed in red shorts. Bonnie said, "Wow," when she saw José come in pulling a wagon loaded with a huge, white bear.

Bonnie laughed when she saw Chee's floppy, brown gorilla. "I don't have a bear," Chee explained. Then, she hugged the old stuffed gorilla and said, "Kong's my favorite!"

Bonnie hugged her bear, too, and thought, "This is going to be a fun day. Everyone will have a great time playing with these toys at school."

Bonnie looked up when she saw Marci come in empty-handed. Marci stopped when she saw the roomful of stuffed animals. Her hands flew up and she cried, "Oh, no! I forgot my bear!"

"Marci feels awful," thought Bonnie. "I would, too, if I forgot my bear. What will she do when it's time to play?"

Suddenly, Bonnie knew what to do. She picked up Grayson and walked toward Marci. She looked at Marci and smiled, "I'm sorry you forgot your bear, Marci. Do you want to hold Grayson for a while? Then, when it's time to play with our animals, we can play with Grayson together."

Marci took the old, brown bear Bonnie held toward her and slowly began to smile. "That'll be fun, Bonnie," Marci said. "Thank you." Then, Marci wiped away her tears with Grayson's paw.

Questions for Discussion

Bonnie and Marci both learned a lot about how it feels to share. Say, "Let's talk about the story and think of some important skills to help us learn more about sharing." Write the skills on the chalkboard or a flip chart as your students respond.

1. Why did Bonnie decide she wanted to share?

   She imagined how bad Marci must feel. (Write **Decide if you want to share.***)*

2. Bonnie did something about Marci's problem right away. Why is it important to share at the right time, when someone has a need?

   She might not have a need later. (Write **Share when someone has a need, not later.***)*

3. Do you always want to share? Why?

   Answers will vary.

4. What did Bonnie do to help Marci not to feel left out?

   shared her bear with Marci (Write **Go to the person and offer to share.***)*

5. Did Bonnie share in a friendly way? How could you tell?

   Yes. She smiled and offered her bear. (Write **Share in a friendly way.***)*

6. What would have happened that day if Bonnie had decided not to share?

   Answers will vary.

Social Skills Activities

Skill A

Decide if You Want to Share

1. Ask your students if they've ever heard the old saying, "Put yourself in the other person's shoes." Explain that it doesn't mean you should actually put on the other person's shoes. It means that you should try to think about how the other person feels and try to feel the same way.

2. Help your students briefly experience being left out. Bring a tray of fruit slices to class. Tell your students how delicious the fruits are going to taste. Then, as your students watch, take a slice of fruit and begin to munch and enjoy the treat. Don't offer to share. Afterwards say, "I didn't share with anyone. I felt bad as I ate my treat in front of you because I imagined how you might be feeling. How did you feel?"

   Say, "Now, let's see how good it feels to be the one who shares." Ask volunteers to hand out the fruit to the rest of the class.

Skill B

Share When Someone Has a Need, Not Later

1. Help your students brainstorm a list of times when they think they'll need to share.

2. Teach your students that they need to share their toys when they invite friends to their homes. Help each student draw a house on a large sheet of paper. Tell them these houses are called Sharing Houses because inside the house they'll draw things they can share when their friends visit. Ask each student to write his name and a friend's name on his Sharing House door.

3. Focus on the fun of sharing when there's a need. Sing "Share-O" to the tune "BINGO."

   There was a person who forgot her umbrella

   And Tonya was her name-o.

   I shared my umbrella, I shared my umbrella, I shared my umbrella

   And Tonya and I stayed dry.

   Now, help your students come up with other verses.

Skill C

Go to the Person and Offer to Share

1. Have your students brainstorm various ways to share. Write their ideas on the chalkboard. For example, your students might say, "I can share my toys with my sister" or "I can share my thoughts with my neighbor."

2. Share work. Say, "Here's an old saying, 'Many hands make light work.' What do you think that saying means?" Explain that sharing work or responsibilities makes work easier for everyone. Have your students share your work by helping you make a bulletin board about sharing. Give half of the students scissors and the other half construction paper. Tell your students you don't have enough materials for everyone, so they'll have to share.

3. Tell your students you brought apples for a snack. Tell them you thought you had enough apples for everyone, but when you got to school, you didn't have enough. Have your students problem solve a fair way for each student to have part of the snack.

4. Designate one day as Share-An-Adventure Day. Explain to your students that, on this day, each student will share a memory. Tell your students to be prepared to tell about trips or adventures they have special memories about. Ask them to bring pictures or other memorabilia about the experience.

Skill D

Share in a Friendly Way

1. Tell your students they'll learn an important word. Write the word *generous* on the chalkboard and describe what it means. Say, "Stand up when you hear the sentence that defines the word *generous*." Then, read these two sentences:

   The man was so generous, he greedily kept all of his things to himself.

   The man was so generous, he happily shared his things when someone needed help.

   Ask your students to tell about times when they've been generous.

2. Help your students recognize friendly sentences. Tell your students to show thumbs-up when you say a friendly, can-get-along sentence and thumbs-down when you say an unfriendly, can't-get-along sentence.

   You push me on the swing, then I'll push you. *up*

   It's mine. *down*

   That's mine! Give it here! *down*

   Do you want some? *up*

   Give it back! *down*

   You can have half of my apple. *up*

   Let's share. *up*

   Give me my hat. *down*

   Do you want to use my crayons? *up*

   Let's build a garage for our car. *up*

Additional Activities

Role-Playing

Review the story in this lesson. Then, select one or both of the following role-play activities.

Choose volunteers to play José and Marci. Pretend that José is the student who shared his white bear with Marci, who forgot her animal. Remind the student playing José to use the skills for sharing. Remind the student playing Marci to say thank you.

Choose volunteers to play Mark and Chee. Pretend that Chee took her crayons home one day after school and forgot to bring them back to school. During art class, she had no crayons. Mark thinks about how he would feel if he had no crayons. He offers to share his crayons. Chee is happy with Mark's offer and they have a good time using Mark's crayons together. Remind the person playing Mark to use the skills for sharing. Remind the person playing Chee to smile and say thank you after Mark offers to share.

Role-Play Feedback

Encourage the rest of your students to give helpful feedback to the role-play volunteers. Use the following questions:

What did you like about each character's part?

What skills did José use for sharing?

What skills did Mark use for sharing?

How did Marci act when José offered to share?

How did Chee act when Mark offered to share?

How could these role plays be different?

Expanding Learning

Use pages 14 through 16 in the Activities Book to help your students improve their skills for sharing by considering the many ways they can share.

Use pages 30 through 37 in the Picture Book to help your students improve their skills for sharing by

- thinking about others as a basis for sharing
- sharing work
- sharing with guests even when your students don't feel like it
- understanding the needs of those who are sick

Use page 17 in the Activities Book to help your students review the skills learned for sharing. Have your students suggest when and how they can practice these skills. For example, a student may say

"I will share with Tonya."

"I will share my umbrella."

"I will ask Tonya if she wants to share my umbrella."

"I will smile when I share."

Visualization

Have your students get in comfortable positions to relax. Then say, "Close your eyes and imagine yourself sharing with a friend.

"Your mom has made some delicious brownies. You have permission to bring a friend home to play after school. When you go to the kitchen and get the brownies, you find there is only one large brownie left. You really want to eat the brownie. But you think, 'My friend will feel bad if I eat the brownie and she has none. I'll share.' So you get two plates and a knife. You try very hard to cut the brownie into two equal pieces.

"You tell your friend, 'Please have a brownie!' Your friend smiles and takes one. Then, you take the other brownie. You sit down, eat your brownies together, and laugh together because it's fun to share with friends. After your friend goes home, your mom tells you, 'I saw the nice way you shared that brownie. That was a friendly thing to do!' You're glad you know how to share."

Lesson 5: Offering Your Help

Skills

A. Decide if the person needs help.

B. Decide how you can help.

C. Ask in a friendly way if you may help.

D. Help a little. Don't take over.

Materials

Activities Book:
pages 18 through 20

Picture Book:
pages 38 through 45

Introduction

Some students don't seem to notice when others need help. Others see their friends' needs, but offer help when they don't need to. There are also those students who don't know how to help. Learning to help is a friendship-making skill that all students need.

It's important for your students to learn that being genuinely helpful can make them feel good. We all need one another. Offering to help others is a positive behavior because it demonstrates that your students can share their things and their time with others. Helping others wins friends because people usually enjoy attention and help.

Goals

In this lesson, your students will learn to sincerely offer help when they see it's both needed and wanted. The activities will help teach your students

- to be aware of valuable abilities they can use to help others
- not to push their help on someone who isn't interested
- not to take over and do it all

Preparation

Observe the way your students offer their help. For example, do any of your students come across as bossy or pushy by insisting that they help another student complete a task? They may need to learn to ask first. Do any students become offended when their help is refused? They need to learn that others may simply want to try it on their own. They must learn to back off gracefully when others refuse their help. Have you noticed any students embarrassing a friend by offering him help in front of others? Students who do this can actually annoy other students in their attempts to help.

Have your students brainstorm how they can help other people and write their answers on the chalkboard. Have your students cut out magazine pictures that show people helping each other. Use the following questions for discussion:

- How could you help a baby?
- How does it feel to help younger people? Older people?
- How have people helped you?
- How do you thank people who help you?

Social Skills Story

Use page 38 in the Picture Book with this story. Introduce the story by focusing on the importance of helping others. Say, "If your classmates offer to help you, you may want to offer to help them, too. Sometimes you can say, 'Do you suppose we can give each other a little help?' That could have happened with Mark and Jonathan one day. But it didn't. Listen to this story."

Jonathan erased his math problem for the fourth time. While erasing, he ripped a hole in his paper. Jonathan got tears in his eyes. "I'm tired of working on this stupid math," he thought. "I'll be glad when we go outside. I can't wait to play soccer. I'm good at soccer!"

Mark finished his last math problem. He checked his answers to be sure they were right. Mark felt proud of his good work as he laid his paper on Mrs. Sahwani's desk. "I'm good at math," thought Mark.

As Mark turned to go back to his desk, he noticed Jonathan erasing his paper. He saw the tears in Jonathan's eyes.

"Jonathan's been having a lot of trouble with math lately," thought Mark. "That's funny. Math seems easy to me and soccer seems easy to Jonathan. But I'm not so good at soccer."

But then Mark did something that surprised even him. As he approached Jonathan, he heard himself saying in a loud voice, "Hey, Jonathan, aren't you done yet? Here, let me do that last problem for you!"

Jonathan's eyes were wide as he looked up to see Mark standing over him. Jonathan's cheeks felt hot. He felt embarrassed when he heard someone laugh as Mark quickly finished Jonathan's last math problem. "Man, I really feel dumb. Mark thinks he's so smart!" thought Jonathan.

Questions for Discussion

Say, "Mark had a perfect chance to be a friend. Instead, his actions upset Jonathan. Let's think of some skills both boys can use next time they offer help." Write the skills on the chalkboard or a flip chart as your students respond.

1. Did Mark think that Jonathan needed help? Why?

   Yes. Jonathan was still working on his math and he had tears in his eyes. (Write **Decide if the person needs help.***)*

2. Did Mark think about the best way to help Jonathan? Why?

   No. He didn't ask if Jonathan needed help; he just did the work for him. (Write **Decide how you can help.***)*

3. Did Mark ask in a friendly way if he could help? How do you know?

   No. He loudly said, "Here, let me do that for you." (Write **Ask in a friendly way if you may help.***)*

4. What did Mark do to embarrass Jonathan?

   He let everyone else know that Jonathan was having trouble.

5. How would Jonathan have felt if Mark had waited until later and said, "Do you suppose we could give each other a little help? You could help me with my soccer kicks and I could help you with math."

   Jonathan would have felt better.

6. It's a good idea not to take over and do it all when you help someone. Why?

   The other person may feel dumb or think you're acting smart if you take over. (Write **Help a little. Don't take over.***)*

Social Skills Activities

Skill A

Decide if the Person Needs Help

1. Here are some ways to increase a spirit of helpfulness in your room. Post this question on a sign in your students' work areas: Would you like some help? Be a good model of helpfulness in your classroom by using phrases like, "May I help you do that?" "Would you like some help?" or "If I help you, we can get this done more quickly." Remember to accept your students' help from time to time and say, "I certainly could use some help with this. Thank you for offering."

2. Have your students spend the day looking for people who might need their help. Refer to the sign, "Would you like some help?" throughout the day. Review or list who needed help and who helped.

3. Talk about friends who always need help. Point out that there are situations when it's particularly easy to help others because help is truly needed. Ask, "Who needs to be remembered with special kindness at all times?" Guide your students to name elderly people in nursing homes, people who are sick, and people with severe handicaps.

   Point out that anyone who is ill or injured needs special help. Ask them to name ways they can help. *Take time to talk with them; carry things for them; bring food or water; read aloud to them; draw pictures for them; turn on or off the television; play music; answers will vary.*

Skill B

Decide How You Can Help

1. You can help increase your students' self-esteem by pointing out that they can help others.

   First, have your students trace their hands on a large sheet of paper. Next, help them write one thing they can do well on each finger of the left hand. Then, help them write one way they can use each skill to help someone on each finger of the right hand. Here's an example:

   Left: I can bowl.
   Right: Teach someone to bowl.

   Left: I write well.
   Right: Help a younger student improve her writing.

   Left: I bake good cookies.
   Right: Share the cookies with someone.

   Left: I'm strong.
   Right: Carry boxes for Mom or Dad.

   Left: I can sing.
   Right: Teach a song to a little child.

2. Have a Mystery Helper's Day. Encourage your students to help others anonymously and enjoy the happy feelings their good deeds bring. Tell them to keep their help a secret from the people they helped, but they can share their happy feelings with you. Here are some ways they can be Mystery Helpers:

   Pick up trash lying around their neighborhoods.

   Do a chore at home without being asked, such as carrying out the garbage or carrying in the groceries.

   Give away some clothing or toys they no longer use (with their parents' permission).

   Give a friend a small gift or make a picture for her. But don't tell her it's from you.

   Draw a pretty picture and take it to someone you don't know in a hospital or nursing home.

   Now, let your students help you think of other ways they can be Mystery Helpers.

3. Play "Little Lost Lion." One student uses a lion puppet (or another animal puppet). Explain that Little Lion is lost and ask what kind of help it needs. Have your students follow the skills for offering help as they help Little Lion find its way home. Have your students think of other reasons Little Lion could need help. Vary the activity by having students role-play the parts of Little Lion and Helper.

Skill C

Ask in a Friendly Way if You May Help

1. Stress the importance of asking if you can help and not taking over and doing the work yourself. Help your students ask with phrases, like "May I help?" or "Do you want some help?" instead of "I'll do that for you."

   Write appropriate phrases like these on the chalkboard:

   Do you want me to help you?

   Would you like some help with that?

   May I give you a hand?

   Could I carry something for you?

   Present the following situations and ask students to respond with one of the phrases above:

   Your friend has to clean her room before she can play.

   You know how to use the computer, but another student isn't sure how to operate the computer.

   A person in a wheelchair has trouble opening a door.

Your parents are very busy and you know how to order pizza.

Mom is sick and must go to bed.

A student is carrying many books.

Skill D

Help a Little. Don't Take Over.

Explain that taking over and doing a job for a friend might make the friend feel unhappy. She may feel dumb. She may think you're being bossy or acting smart. Have your students show thumbs-up when you describe a situation where someone is helpful. Have them show thumbs-down when the person is taking over.

May I help you carry these books to the library? *up*

Here, I'll finish your story for you. *down*

I'd like to bring you a bowl of soup if it's okay. *up*

May I feed your cat for you while you're gone? *up*

Move over. I'll wash your dog for you. *down*

Additional Activities

Role-Playing

Review the story in this lesson. Then, select one or both of the following role-play activities.

Choose volunteers to play Jonathan and Mark. Pretend Mark tells Jonathan that he'll help him with his math if Jonathan helps him with his soccer kick. Remind the person playing Mark to ask if Jonathan needs help in a friendly way. Remind Mark not to do all the work for Jonathan.

Choose volunteers to play Bonnie and José. Pretend that José is walking toward the library carrying an armful of books. One book tumbles off the stack and falls to the floor just as he gets to the closed door. Across the hall, Bonnie sees José's problem and quickly walks over to offer help. Remind the student playing Bonnie to ask José in a friendly way if he needs help.

Role-Play Feedback

Encourage the rest of your students to give helpful feedback to the role-play volunteers. Use the following questions:

What did you like about each character's part?

What skills did Mark use for offering help?

What skills did Bonnie use for offering help?

How did Jonathan respond to Mark's help?

How did José respond to Bonnie's help?

How could these role plays be different?

Expanding Learning

Use pages 18 and 19 in the Activities Book to help your students

- ask first before helping someone
- decide upon help that's appropriate

Use pages 38 through 45 in the Picture Book to help your students improve skills for helping others by

- helping without taking over
- offering help in private to avoid embarrassing friends
- noticing when someone needs help
- helping those who are sick, injured, or handicapped

Use page 20 in the Activities Book to help your students review the skills they have learned for offering their help to others. Have your students suggest when and how they will practice these skills. For example, your students may say

"I think Mrs. Sahwani needs help."

"I could help wash the chalkboard."

"May I help you wash the chalkboard?"

"I will wash the part that I can reach."

Visualization

Have your students get in comfortable positions to relax. Then say, "Close your eyes and imagine yourself offering to help a classmate use the computer.

"You're good at using the computer. You notice the other student is trying to start the new program, but nothing is happening. As you watch, you see that she is using the wrong keys. You smile and walk over to your classmate. In a friendly voice you say, 'Would you like some help with that?'

"She smiles and says, 'I would!' You say, 'These are the keys you should press to start the program. I'll write them down for you so you can remember.' Your friend looks grateful. 'Thanks a lot,' she says. 'Sure. Anytime!' you respond. You feel good and you're glad you know how to offer help to others."

Lesson 6: Saying You're Sorry

Skills

A. Admit it when you make a mistake.

B. Go to the person as soon as possible.

C. Sincerely say you're sorry.

D. Make up for your mistake when you can.

Materials

Activities Book:
pages 21 through 23

Picture Book:
pages 46 through 53

Introduction

Some students have difficulty admitting they're wrong. However, they need to learn to admit their mistakes in order to get along with others. When your students quickly and sincerely admit their mistakes, they'll learn that most people will forgive them. These students also need to learn that repeated misbehavior requires more than "I'm sorry." It demands a change in their behavior. Your students can strengthen their friendships by recognizing and making up for their mistakes.

Apologizing is a difficult task. It takes courage to say, "I'm sorry I hurt you. I didn't mean to." It also takes honesty for your students to acknowledge their own errors. And even when your students are honest and courageously admit a mistake, they have to know the words to say in apology.

Some students may apologize too much. They may feel bad for events they didn't cause. For example, a student may feel responsible if she got sick and her family couldn't go on vacation.

It's important for your students to learn skills for handling their own errors, whether accidental or intentional. Your students will feel better after apologizing and making up for their mistakes.

Goals

In this lesson, your students will improve skills for sincerely saying they're sorry. This lesson is based on the premise, "When you're wrong, admit it." The activities will help your students

- admit their mistakes when they're wrong
- learn how to make up for their mistakes
- learn how to say they're sorry

Preparation

Create an atmosphere that encourages your students to sympathize with one another by apologizing when you make mistakes. When you say, "I'm sorry I forgot to bring that book I promised. I'll write myself a note so I'll be sure to bring it tomorrow," you're modeling an important skill for your students.

Discuss the importance of apologizing by talking about the Golden Rule. Explain that "Do unto others as you would have them do unto you" is an old saying. Point out that this is such an important idea that it has been called the Golden Rule so people will remember to follow it.

Ask your students, "Why do you think it's important to say you're sorry when you haven't been nice to someone else?" Then, ask "What do you think our school would be like if no one ever said 'I'm sorry' or 'Please excuse me'? "

Social Skills Story

Use page 46 in the Picture Book with this story. Say, "Have you ever felt terrible because you did something wrong? Was it hard to know what to do? It was hard for Chee. Listen to this story."

Chee's grandfather gave her a $10 bill on her birthday before she went to school. Chee's grandfather said, "Put your money in your drawer so you won't lose it. We'll go shopping in a few days and you can spend it however you wish."

Chee thought, "I'm older now, and Grandfather doesn't know how well I can take care of money. I'll just put the money in my purse and show it to my friends today. I'll bring the money back and put it away after school."

Chee put the $10 bill in her purse, but she forgot to snap her purse when she hurried outside to meet the bus. When Chee was getting on the school bus, the money fell out of her purse.

When Chee got to school, she realized she'd lost her money. She felt terrible. She wished she'd listened to her grandfather.

"What will I say to Grandfather?" Chee asked herself. She felt very bad about not listening to her grandfather. And she felt bad about losing the money.

Three days passed. Chee was afraid that her grandfather would yell at her, so she didn't say a word about her mistake.

Then, one afternoon Grandfather said, "Chee, you look sad and gloomy. Is anything wrong?"

"Oh, nothing's wrong," said Chee and she tried to smile.

Finally, at the end of the week, her grandfather asked again, "Is anything wrong, Chee? I don't see your happy smile very much lately."

Chee couldn't keep it from her grandfather any longer. She began to cry. "Please don't yell. I'm very sorry. I lost the $10 you gave me."

Chee's grandfather said, "Chee, I'm not going to yell. Losing $10 makes you feel sad. If you'd listened to me, you wouldn't have lost it. You've gone around for a week feeling terrible about what you did. You punished yourself by feeling so bad. You didn't have to do that. I wish you'd told me right away as soon as you lost your money."

Chee felt so much better for finally telling her grandfather how sorry she was.

Questions for Discussion

Ask your students, "What do you think Chee learned about saying 'I'm sorry'?" Then say, "Now let's see if we can think of the skills Chee could use the next time she needs to apologize." Write the skills on the chalkboard or a flip chart as your students respond.

1. Everyone makes mistakes sometimes. Why do you think it's so hard to admit our mistakes?

   Someone might get mad at us. We're afraid to. (Write **Admit it when you make a mistake.***)*

2. Why did Chee wait so long to tell her grandfather she was sorry?

   She was afraid he would yell at her.

3. When did Chee's grandfather say he wished Chee had come to tell him about her mistake? Why?

   Right away. She wouldn't have to feel so bad for so long. (Write **Go to the person as soon as possible.***)*

4. Did Chee really mean it when she told her grandfather she was sorry? How could you tell?

   Yes. Her tears and her words showed she was sincere. (Write **Sincerely say you're sorry.***)*

5. What does *sincere* mean?

   It means honest, real, not fake.

6. Could Chee do anything to make up for her mistake?

   Answers will vary. Explain that sometimes there's nothing you can do to change what happened. For example, Chee couldn't find the money she lost. Her sincere apology was all she could do.

7. How can people make up for their mistakes?

   They could offer to fix, pay for, or replace something they've broken; answers will vary. (Write **Make up for your mistake when you can.***)*

Social Skills Activities

Skill A

Admit It When You Make a Mistake

1. Help your students see others' mistakes. Have students bring cartoons to class that show the mistakes of characters. Ask your students to explain what the characters did wrong and how they could admit their mistakes.

2. Discuss familiar stories such as "The Little Red Hen." Read the story and ask your students to name the mistakes. Ask whether the characters' mistakes were accidental or on purpose. Point out that most mistakes can be forgiven. But sometimes, you have to live with the results of your mistakes, like the animals in the story did.

3. Help your students know when to apologize by understanding when they're at fault. Read the following situations to your students. Have them answer yes or no to tell if it was the student's fault when these things happened.

   Sandy hit a baseball through the neighbor's window. *yes*

   Dustin got chicken pox and his family couldn't go on their vacation. *no*

   Amanda spilled milk on the living room carpet. Amanda wasn't allowed to bring food in the living room. *yes*

   Gloria practiced hard for the choir contest. The choir didn't win. *no*

Skill B
Go to the Person as Soon as Possible

1. Suggest to your students that the best way to keep friends after a disagreement is to talk things out. Say to your students, "If you hurt your friends, but didn't mean to, say you're sorry. If your friends embarrassed you, let them know how you feel so they won't do it again. Clear up any misunderstandings right away." Suggest that it's hard to ask forgiveness, but there are several ways to get started. Offer these examples:

   "I don't blame you for being mad at me. That was a stupid thing I did."

   "It's really hard for me to say this, but I'm so sorry for saying something mean about you to Cory."

   "I can't believe I forgot. I'm sorry I didn't invite you to my party."

2. Suggest that your students write notes to friends if they're having trouble talking to them. Have your students practice writing an imaginary friend a short letter of apology. They could use some of the sentences above in their letters adding, "I hope we can still be friends."

3. Admit small mistakes with simple comments or humor. Point out that when we tell others that we already know we goofed, they generally forget about finding fault. Ask your students to match the situations below to the comments you provide. First, write these comments on the chalkboard or put them on cards and hand them out to various students:

   "I'm sorry I bumped you. Just call me Grace!" (Explain the figurative language.)

   "Hi, gang. I'm as slow as a turtle today. I'm really sorry I'm late."

   "Excuse me, please. I was just so excited to tell you what's been happening."

   Here are the situations:

   You're late joining your friends after school for a game of softball. They've been waiting for you for 30 minutes.

   You've interrupted your friend several times.

   You bumped into someone in the lunch line.

Skill C
Sincerely Say You're Sorry

1. An Eastern proverb says, "If you're going to bow, bow low." Your students may not understand this proverb, but they can understand its spirit. Insincere apologies aren't apologies at all. Have your students brainstorm ways they can let people know they're truly sorry.

2. Discuss how your students can accept apologies from others. Ask them, "Would you think the other person is truly sorry if you heard these apologies?"

   I'm really sorry. I thought you knew I had to leave early today. *yes*

   SOR – RY! (yelling) *no*

   I'm sorry I forgot your birthday. I can't imagine forgetting someone as nice as you. *yes*

   I didn't mean to! (yelling and walking away) *no*

   (sigh) That's just the way it happens sometimes. *no*

   Pardon me for running into you. Are you okay? *yes*

3. Say to your students, "It takes honesty and courage to admit your errors. If someone admits a mistake to you, go out of your way to make him feel at ease. List some responses your students can make to accept apologies. Have them make up situations to match each response.

   Don't worry about it.

   That's okay. Everyone makes mistakes sometimes.

   Thanks for apologizing.

   I understand.

   That's okay. It was an accident.

   That's okay. We're still friends.

   Have your students role-play saying the responses.

Skill D

Make Up for Your Mistake When You Can

1. Saying you're sorry over and over for the same mistake wears out any friendship.

   Your students must understand that sometimes saying sorry isn't enough. They must make amends or change their behavior.

   Say to your students, "Pretend to be the person in each situation I read. How could you make up for the mistake?"

   You spilled some juice on your grandmother's sofa.

   You yelled at your younger brother and made him cry.

   You embarrassed your friend when you said she was as skinny as a bean pole.

   You took something that didn't belong to you.

   You had permission to use your friend's skateboard, but you scratched it when you ran into something.

   You used your sister's new bath powder, tipped the box over, and dropped it into the bathtub.

   You spilled chocolate milk all over the clean kitchen floor.

Additional Activities

Role-Playing

Review the story in this lesson. Then, select one or both of the following role-play activities.

Choose volunteers to play Chee and her grandfather. Pretend Chee tells her grandfather right away that she lost her money. Remind the person playing Chee to show that she is sorry. Remind the person playing Chee's grandfather to accept Chee's apology if she's sincere.

Choose volunteers to play Mark and Marci. Pretend that Mark borrowed Marci's tape, used it, and returned it. Mark didn't realize the tape had broken as he was rewinding it. When Marci tried to play the tape the next day, she noticed it was broken. Remind the person playing Mark to use all the skills he's learned for saying he's sorry.

Role-Play Feedback

Encourage the rest of your students to give helpful feedback to the role-play volunteers. Use the following questions:

What did you like about each character's part?

What skills for saying you're sorry did Chee use?

Was Mark sincere when he told Marci he was sorry?

What did Marci say to Mark after he said he was sorry?

How could these role plays be different?

Expanding Learning

Use pages 21 and 22 in the Activities Book to help your students improve their skills for saying they're sorry by

- admitting their mistakes
- responding appropriately when someone asks them for forgiveness

Use pages 46 through 53 in the Picture Book to help your students improve their apologizing skills by

- understanding that everyone makes mistakes and the best thing to do is admit it right away and ask for forgiveness
- realizing that when people don't admit their own mistakes, they won't have many friends
- seeing the difference between a sincere and an insincere apology
- discussing what can be done to make up for a mistake when they've broken something or become angry

Use page 23 in the Activities Book to help your students review the skills for saying they're sorry. Have your students suggest when and how they can practice these skills. For example they may say

"I am late."

"I will go to Marci."

"I am sorry I'm late, Marci. I forgot to look at the clock."

"I will come earlier next time to make up for our lost time."

Visualization

Have your students get in comfortable positions to relax. Then say, "Close your eyes and imagine yourself helping someone feel better because you know how to say you're sorry.

"One morning at school, you were in such a hurry to get into the library with your overdue book that you forgot to open the door carefully. When you came to the library door, you threw it open, just as a younger student was about to go out the door. The door bumped the younger student on her forehead, and she began to cry. Her books fell to the floor.

"As you picked up her books, you said, 'I'm really sorry I hurt you. I'll walk back to your room with you.' As you walked down the hallway together, you saw a water fountain and asked if she'd like to get a drink of water. She drank some water. Then, she looked at you and smiled. 'Thanks. I'm all right now. I can go on by myself.' You told her good-bye and started back to the library. You felt glad you knew how to say you're sorry."

Lesson 7: Giving Compliments

Skills

A. Say something nice that's really true.

B. Look at the person and smile.

C. Say it clearly in a friendly way.

Materials

Activities Book:
pages 24 through 27

Picture Book:
pages 54 through 61

Introduction

Many students rarely give compliments because giving compliments is a skill that is rarely taught. Some students might not know how to give straightforward compliments. Instead, they sarcastically say things like, "Nice hat, Marla. Where did you get it?" The same comment sincerely spoken, of course, would be a compliment. Others avoid giving compliments because they feel embarrassed. Sadly, complimenting others is also difficult because most people have difficulty receiving compliments graciously.

Goals

In this lesson, your students will learn to give sincere compliments. The activities will help your students

- learn to use positive words
- learn to use appropriate body language

Preparation

Compliments are gifts of praise. Praise may be the greatest gift you can give your students. It builds their self-esteem and empowers them. Focus on the positive aspects of every child. Create an atmosphere which makes it easy to give compliments by being kind, cheerful, and even-tempered. Help your students appreciate everyone's best qualities, even their own. After all, students who appreciate themselves won't be shy about passing along compliments to others.

Make and display a banner that says: Friends Appreciate Each Other. Explain that you *appreciate* someone when you look for and admire good things in that person. Suggest that your students can appreciate themselves just as they appreciate one another.

Have your students think of one thing they appreciate about themselves. Then, have them think of one good thing they appreciate about someone sitting near to them.

Say, "You can show your friends you appreciate them by telling them one good thing. Just start your sentence, 'I like _______.' Saying nice things to each other is called giving compliments. When someone tells you something nice, you say, 'Thank you.' "

Suggest that your students can tell when they've received a compliment because it feels good. A compliment is more than just nice words. It's nice words given in a friendly way.

The person giving the compliment is usually looking at you and smiling.

Giving compliments is a way of helping others feel good. A compliment is something nice you say about a person. It feels like a gift.

Social Skills Story

Use page 54 in the Picture Book with this story. Ask, "What nice thing has someone told you about yourself? How did you feel when you heard that nice compliment?" Then say, "José heard a lot of nice things about himself from his parents. That's why he felt like telling someone else something nice. Listen to this story."

José went into the kitchen to have some cereal with his mom, his stepdad, and his grandpa. His older brother and sister had already gone to school.

José was dressed for school. José's mom smiled when she saw him and said, "You're all dressed, José. You've already combed your hair, too. You look great!"

"Thanks, Mom," José said.

José's grandpa watched José begin to eat. "José, I've got to mend that squeaky front door to our apartment. I'll wait till you get home from school so you can help. You're such a big help," José's grandpa said.

"Okay, great!" said José. He liked helping his grandpa. He smiled to himself, "Grandpa likes my help because I'm good at finding his tools for him. I like helping Grandpa. Maybe I'll be a carpenter when I grow up."

José finished his cereal and grabbed his lunch box. José and his stepdad, Victor, walked out the door together. Victor smiled at José and said, "You're a great son. Good-bye, my friend."

José felt warm inside. Victor always called him friend. "That's because he likes doing things with me," thought José.

José smiled. "Bye, Victor. See you tonight," he said.

José said good-bye to his mom and grandpa and left for school. The nice things his family had told him that morning made José feel good.

During music class that day, the music teacher, Mr. Lenski, told the class, "Today we'll have a special class. Chee will play the piano for us. It's the same music she played in the city contest!"

José watched Chee play the piano. "How did she learn to play the piano so well?" José wondered.

When Chee hit the last note, all the students clapped. They loved her music. José wanted to tell Chee how great he thought her music was. But when he saw her as they left music class, he just smiled. He felt embarrassed. He didn't know what to say.

Questions for Discussion

Say, "Let's think of skills José could have used for complimenting Chee." Write the skills on the chalkboard or a flip chart as your students respond.

1. True or false? A compliment is something nice you say about someone that's really true.

   true

2. Name at least one compliment José received.

   José's mom liked his hair; José's grandpa liked the way he helped him; Victor said he was a great son.

3. Should you always say things that are true in your compliments? Why?

   Yes. If you give compliments that aren't true, others will think you're just "buttering them up." After a while they won't believe you. (Write **Say something nice that's really true.***)*

4. Does this sound like a compliment? Sarcastically say, "Nice shoes. Where'd you get them?" Why?

   No. It sounds like you're making fun of the shoes.

5. How could you say the same words as a compliment?

   Smile, look at the person, and use a friendly tone of voice. (Write **Look at the person and smile.***)*

6. How can you say a compliment so the person is sure to hear what you say?

   Say it clearly in a friendly way. (Write **Say it clearly in a friendly way.***)*

7. Why didn't José tell Chee he liked her piano music?

   He felt embarrassed; he didn't know what to say.

Social Skills Activities

Skill A

Say Something Nice That's Really True

1. Compare a compliment to a gift. Say, "When you get a compliment, it feels like you're getting a gift." Discuss that a compliment is something nice you say to someone. We give compliments to help others feel good about themselves. Talk about how we feel when we get compliments.

2. Brainstorm and list the kinds of things that people usually give compliments to each other about. Include appearance, possessions, personal qualities, and abilities.

3. Writing compliments is an easy way to get used to giving compliments. Help your students write compliments by making a Compliments Book. Tell them they're going to write compliments in the other students' books. Each student will get to keep her own book. Give your students half sheets of colored construction paper, one for each student in the class. Help them complete this sentence about each student: "My favorite thing about (student's name) is the way _____." Or, "I like the way (student's name) _____."

   Have your students decorate each page and give it to the student the page belongs to. When they're done, bind the pages together with clips, staples, or yarn. Then, have your students decorate the cover with the words, "My Compliments Book."

4. Help your students write notes to school helpers, family members, or friends complimenting things they do to help.

Skill B

Look at the Person and Smile

1. Point out that smiling while giving a compliment makes the compliment look and sound friendly. Show the difference a smile makes in one's voice. Help your students say several sentences into a tape recorder. First, they should say some sentences without smiling. Then, they should repeat the sentences with a smile. Comment on the difference in the tone of voice.

2. Cut out smiley faces from colored construction paper. Leave space for a short sentence on each one. Give each student a face. Help them write one compliment about another student in the class. Later, have each student stand, face the person, read the statement, and hand the face to that person.

   Students may wear the smiles or you may use them to make a bulletin board featuring compliments. To ensure that each student receives a smile, students may draw names to determine who to write about.

Skill C

Say It Clearly in a Friendly Way

1. Help your students distinguish between compliments and sarcastic remarks. Say, "A compliment is given in a friendly way. How can you be sure to say something in a friendly way? *Say it with a nice smile and look the person in the eye.* Then, demonstrate two ways of saying the same words, once sarcastically and once sincerely. Ask, "Is this a sincere compliment?" Answer yes or no.

   "Nice shirt!" (roll eyes and say sarcastically) *no*

   "I like your haircut." (sincerely with smile) *yes*

   "Great story. What an imagination!" (sincerely) *yes*

   "Wow. What a bike." (laugh sarcastically) *no*

2. Have each student circulate around the room and compliment five other students you have chosen. Your students must say the compliments clearly.

Additional Activities

Role-Playing

Review the story in this lesson. Then, select one or both of the following role-play activities.

Choose volunteers to play José and Chee. Pretend that José tells Chee that he likes her music. Remind the student playing José to smile and use friendly words. A good way to begin a compliment is to say, "I like . . . ."

Choose volunteers to play Bonnie and Jonathan. Pretend that Bonnie notices a picture Jonathan has drawn. She likes the planes in the sky and the airport on the ground. It reminds her of a plane trip she once took. Remind the student playing Bonnie to smile and use friendly words.

Role-Play Feedback

Encourage the rest of your students to give helpful feedback to the role-play volunteers. Use the following questions:

What did you like about each character's part?

Which skills for giving compliments did José use?

How did Chee respond to the compliment?

Which skills for giving compliments did Bonnie use?

How did Jonathan respond to the compliment?

How could these role plays be different?

Expanding Learning

Use pages 24 through 26 in the Activities Book to help your students improve their skills for giving compliments by

- distinguishing between good and poor compliments
- finding something nice about friends to compliment

Use pages 54 through 61 in the Picture Book to help your students

- define "compliment" and tell why we give them
- practice changing statements into compliments that include a positive word
- practice generating compliments about their positive thoughts about friends
- think of ways to compliment family members

Use page 27 in the Activities Book to help your students review the skills for giving compliments. Have your students suggest when and how they can practice these skills. For example, they may say

"I will say, 'I love your new blouse.' "

"I will look and smile at Mona."

"I will use a friendly voice."

Visualization

Have your students get in comfortable positions to relax. Then say, "Close your eyes and imagine yourself giving a friend a compliment.

"You want to say you enjoyed your friend's neat party. You don't feel embarrassed because you remember how good it feels to hear something nice. You know that a compliment is a way of helping others feel good.

"So you smile, look at your friend, and say, 'I liked your party!' Then, you wait just a moment. Your friend smiles back at you and says, 'Thanks a lot. I'm glad you had a good time!' When you're done, you feel good. You're glad you know how to give a compliment to your friend."

Lesson 8: Accepting Compliments

Skills

A. When you hear someone give you a compliment, listen carefully.

B. Say thank you for the compliment in a friendly way.

C. Add a few more words if you can.

Materials

Activities Book:
pages 28 through 30

Picture Book:
pages 62 through 69

Introduction

Your students probably like receiving compliments, but they might have trouble knowing what to do when they get them. They may feel embarrassed and not know what to say when someone gives them a compliment. They may be unable to believe compliments because they have low self-esteem. Whatever the cause, your students may respond to compliments by shrugging them off, ignoring or arguing with the people who gave them the compliment, or giving someone else the credit.

Compliments can be powerful self-esteem builders, if your students listen to and accept them. Teach your students to graciously say thank you to compliments.

Goals

In this lesson, your students will learn how to accept compliments. The activities will teach your students to

- listen when they receive compliments
- say thank you without denying, refusing, or putting the compliments down
- learn ways to look and sound as if they mean it when they say thank you

Preparation

Teach your students to accept compliments by accepting them yourself. Learn to accept a compliment as you would accept a gift. Untie its ribbon, take out the tissue paper, peek inside, and take out the lovely present. Learn to value positive comments from others and use them to nourish your own self-esteem. Then, when you hear, "Thanks for all the extra time you put into the student program," you'll respond with, "Thanks. I enjoy working hard on something so important!" When you've become adept at accepting compliments, you'll be the model your students need.

Say to your students, "What should you say when someone gives you a compliment? It's easy if you use the right words, right tone of voice, and right body language. The right words are thank you, the right tone of voice is friendly, and the right body language is to smile and sit up straight.

"Now, I'm going to say something nice about you. Let's see what you say back to me. This should be fun." Then, give your students compliments that are easy to accept, such as "I like your new shoes" or "I like your pretty brown hair." At this point, praise their simple "thank-yous." Later, your students will learn to smile, use eye contact, and add a few more words.

Social Skills Story

Use page 62 in the Picture Book with this story. Ask, "How do you feel when someone says something nice about you? What do you think will happen if you don't accept compliments?" Say, "Jonathan knew how to receive compliments. They made him feel great. But let's see how Mark felt. Listen to this story."

On Monday night while supper was in the oven, Jonathan and his dad sat at the kitchen table to do their homework. Jonathan was thinking about a story he was writing for Mrs. Sahwani. He liked studying with his dad because his dad was a college student and he had to study, too.

Jonathan and his dad looked up when Jonathan's mom came home from work. She sniffed the air and smiled. "What's that wonderful smell?" she asked.

Jonathan grinned. "It's called Chicken Marvelous," he said.

When Mom went to change her clothes, Jonathan and his dad cleared the books from the table, filled three plates with the hot chicken and vegetables, and told Mom supper was ready. Then, all three sat down to eat their supper.

Jonathan smiled when his mom took a bite, looked at his dad and said, "This is good! It's so nice to come home to a delicious supper after work."

Jonathan's dad listened and smiled as he looked at Jonathan's mom. "Thanks! I'm glad you like it."

Then, Dad complimented Jonathan. "You were a big help, son. You got the ingredients out for me, and that saved time. We got it done in no time."

Jonathan felt proud. "Mom and Dad have a lot of work to do. I'm glad I'm old enough to help," he thought. Then, he sat up straight, looked at his dad, and clearly said, "Thanks, Dad. I like helping you."

Then, he looked at his mom and said, "Your new T-shirt looks neat, Mom."

"Thanks, Jonathan. I'm glad you noticed," she said.

The next morning at school, Jonathan helped Mark with his soccer.

Jonathan watched Mark swing through with a great kick. The ball sped across the playground perfectly. Jonathan yelled, "Great, Mark. Way to kick!"

But Mark just shrugged, looked down at the ground, and mumbled, "I could have done better."

Jonathan was confused and thought, "Doesn't Mark know how much he's improved?"

Questions for Discussion

Say, "Let's talk about receiving compliments and think of skills that Mark can use next time he gets a compliment." Write the skills on the chalkboard or a flip chart as your students respond.

1. What compliments did you hear in this story?

   Jonathan's mom liked the food; his dad liked Jonathan's help; Jonathan liked his mom's T-shirt; Jonathan liked Mark's soccer kick.

2. What's the first thing Jonathan's dad did when Jonathan's mom complimented him?

   He listened. (Write **When you hear someone give you a compliment, listen carefully.***)*

3. What does it mean to *accept* a compliment?

   You take time to listen, believe it, and say thank you.

4. When Jonathan complimented Mark's soccer kick, did Mark accept Jonathan's compliment? How could you tell?

   No. He didn't say thank you; he just looked at the ground and said he thought he could have done better.

5. True or false? Jonathan thanked his dad in a friendly way for complimenting him. How could you tell?

   True. Jonathan sat up straight, looked at his dad, and clearly said, "Thanks." (Write **Say thank you for the compliment in a friendly way.***)*

6. If someone complimented you on your shirt, what would you say besides thank you?

   Answers will vary. (Write **Add a few more words if you can.***)*

Social Skills Activities

Skill A

When You Hear Someone Give You a Compliment, Listen Carefully

1. Discuss the meaning of *accept*. Tell your students that *accept* means to take something after it has been given to you. Then, compare accepting a compliment to accepting a gift. Ask, "How are a gift and a compliment alike? How are they different?" Then say, "A compliment is a spoken gift. It's important to take a gift. If you don't, you may hurt the feelings of the person giving it to you. It's the same with compliments. Others won't want to compliment you if you won't take their compliments." Add that it's easy to accept a compliment by just saying thanks.

2. Try role reversal. Say, "Listen carefully. Then, accept a compliment. Let's practice by changing roles. I'll be you accepting a compliment and you be your friend." Then, have your student compliment you:

   Student: I like the way you read that story.

   Teacher (playing role of student): Thank you. I'm glad you liked it.

3. Try prompts and cues. Tell your students exactly what to say if they continue to have difficulty accepting compliments. For example, say "Here's a compliment. 'You've made great improvements in your handwriting.' To accept the compliment say, 'Thanks. I've been working hard at it.' "

4. Sometimes students will think they aren't receiving compliments when actually they receive many compliments. They're just not hearing the compliments. Have your

students keep a list of all the nice things people say about them.

Skill B

Say Thank You for the Compliment in a Friendly Way

1. Draw a simple stick figure on the chalkboard to emphasize eye contact, posture, and clear speech. Draw arrows to the figure's eyes, posture, and speech. Then, label the eyes *Look*, the shoulders *Sit tall*, and the mouth *Thank you*.

   Use the stick figure to remind your students how to practice saying a friendly thank you as you read these statements:

   It was nice of you to write that note to me.

   I like how you speak so clearly.

   I'm glad to have you in my class.

   You listened so well during story time.

   You look great in that color.

   You're improving your skills in accepting and giving compliments.

   That's a nice shirt.

   I like your smile. It makes me feel happy.

   Thanks for bringing your mom. I enjoyed meeting her.

Skill C

Add a Few More Words if You Can

1. Before you do this activity, write the following sentences on strips of paper. Next, have volunteers read each compliment to you. Then, model the response. Afterwards, do a role reversal. You give the compliments and ask your students to add a few words to their thank yous.

   Compliments:

   I like your shoes.

   Your desk looks neat.

   You were a good friend when you waited to sit by me on the bus.

   You've used great colors on your picture.

   I'm glad you worked so hard on your story. It's great.

   Responses:

   Thanks very much. I like them, too.

   Thanks. I've been trying hard to keep it neat.

   Thanks. I like sitting by you, too.

   Thanks. I like the colors, too.

   Thank you. I like working hard on special projects.

Additional Activities

Role-Playing

Review the story in this lesson. Then, select one or both of the following role-play activities.

Choose volunteers to play Jonathan and Mark. Pretend that Mark accepts Jonathan's compliment about his great soccer kick. Remind the student playing Mark to accept the compliment by saying thanks and by using good body language.

Choose volunteers to play José and Chee. Pretend that José notices that Chee is a fast runner. José tells Chee that he hopes they get to run together on a relay team on Field Day. Remind the student playing Chee to say thank you in a friendly way and add a few more words.

Role-Play Feedback

Encourage the rest of your students to give helpful feedback to the role-play volunteers. Use the following questions:

What did you like about each character's part?

What skills did Mark use for accepting compliments?

Did José give his compliment in a friendly way? How could you tell?

Which skills for accepting compliments did Chee use?

Did Chee sound and look as if she meant her thank you? How could you tell?

How could these role plays be different?

Expanding Learning

Use pages 28 and 29 in the Activities Book to help your students

- accept compliments in a friendly way
- choose appropriate ways to respond to compliments

Use pages 62 through 69 in the Picture Book to help your students

- learn why it's important to accept compliments
- accept compliments sincerely
- review the skills for accepting compliments
- learn to add a few words to the thank you when accepting compliments

Use page 30 in the Activities Book to help your students review the skills for accepting compliments. Have your students suggest when and how they can practice these skills. For example, they may say

"I heard my teacher say she liked my math work."

"I will say thank you and look at my teacher."

"I will say thank you, I have been practicing it."

Visualization

Have your students get in comfortable positions to relax. Then say, "Close your eyes and imagine yourself really listening to a compliment.

"Last week, your teacher told you that you needed to improve your handwriting. Since then, you've practiced hard on your handwriting every day. Today, your teacher stopped at your desk and said, 'You've been practicing your handwriting. I can see that it's improving.'

"You listen carefully to the compliment. Then, sitting up straight in your desk, you look at your teacher and say, 'Thanks. I've really been trying. I'm glad you noticed!' Your teacher smiles broadly and walks to her desk. You feel great. You tell yourself, 'I'm glad I know how to accept compliments. Compliments feel good.' "

Fitting In at School

Learning how to fit in at school has been called "the hidden curriculum of the classroom." That's because it's something students are expected to do but are rarely taught. To fit in at school, students must know what their teacher expects and how to meet those expectations successfully.

Most teachers have three basic expectations for their students:

- try hard
- follow the rules
- communicate effectively with both peers and teachers

In essence, teachers expect students to become independent learners.

The students who fit in well usually have the social language skills and thinking skills that make them academically and socially acceptable. There are positive rewards for fitting in.

The students who don't fit in receive criticism and experience failure. In our schools, students who don't fit in are generally referred for diagnostic or medical evaluation. These students usually haven't met curriculum objectives or expectations for communicative interaction.

The lessons in Unit 2 will help your students survive in the classroom through practice with the following social language skills:

Lesson 1: Paying attention in class.

Lesson 2: Asking for help, but only after first trying to do an activity alone.

Lesson 3: Showing appreciation for help given by friends or teachers.

Lesson 4: Following the teacher's directions.

Lesson 5: Asking questions appropriately to gain information or clarify statements.

Lesson 6: Participating meaningfully in classroom discussions and activities.

Lesson 7: Completing assignments on time.

Lesson 1: Being a Good Listener

Skills

A. Look at the speaker.

B. Be still.

C. Nod your head.

D. Think about what the speaker is saying.

E. Ask questions.

Materials

Activities Book:
pages 32 through 34

Picture Book:
pages 70 through 77

Introduction

Students who have difficulty listening often don't understand that listening takes a lot of work. They may give the speaker only partial attention or even do other things while someone is talking to them.

In order for students to become better listeners, they have to become active listeners. Active listeners use the skills that will be taught in this lesson. Active listeners usually enjoy social and academic success. They listen with their ears, their eyes, and their hearts. They listen for information as well as for feelings.

Goals

In this lesson, your students will improve skills for active listening. The activities will help your students to

- use appropriate body language to show they're listening
- learn to show the speaker that they got the message

Preparation

Introduce the concept of active listening. Compare listening and speaking to catching and throwing a baseball. Ask, "Which is more important to do, throw the ball or catch it?" Of course, both are needed. Without both players participating, the game can't be played.

Point out that in a conversation, the listener must work hard to receive the message from the speaker. Ask, "What must a listener do to understand what the speaker says?"

Social Skills Story

Use page 70 in the Picture Book with this story. Tell your students that good listeners must put aside their own thoughts and try to understand the speaker's thoughts. Say, "Did you ever miss out on something because you didn't listen? That's what happened to Marci when Bonnie's dad visited their classroom. Listen to this story."

Bonnie's dad came to talk to the students in Room 14 about his work as a fire fighter. He wore a black uniform with a black helmet and black boots. He carried a yellow fire coat, a fire fighter's mask, and an air pack.

Bonnie's dad set the mask and the air pack on a desk at the front of the room and said, "This mask saved my life last week! Would you like to know how?" The students nodded their heads eagerly, sat very still, and looked at Bonnie's dad as he talked. They could hardly wait to hear the fire fighter's story!

Meanwhile, across the room, Marci looked out the window and began to daydream. "I'll be a fire fighter some day," Marci thought. "I'll roar down the street behind the wheel of a shiny yellow fire engine. The sirens will be screaming. Cars will pull over to let me pass." She imagined herself pulling up to a flaming apartment building. She thought, "I'll grab my mask and yell orders to the other fire fighters while we're jumping off the truck!" Then, Marci remembered the mask that saved Bonnie's dad's life. "I wonder how it saved his life," Marci thought. Marci sat up in her seat. She could hear Bonnie asking her dad a question.

Bonnie asked, "Can women be fire fighters?"

"Of course they can," he said. "Anyone can be a fire fighter as long as she has a strong body and learns not to fear fire."

Marci was glad she had heard that. She could hardly wait until recess so she could pretend to be a fire fighter. Still, she wished she had heard the story about how the mask had saved Bonnie's dad's life.

Questions for Discussion

Say, "Let's think of the skills Marci can follow next time to help her listen better." Write the skills on the chalkboard or a flip chart as your students respond.

1. Who had difficulty listening in this story?

   Marci

2. What were the good listeners doing with their eyes to show the fire fighter they were listening?

   looking at him (Write **Look at the speaker.***)*

3. What were some other ways the students showed the speaker they were listening?

   nodded their heads, sat still (Write **Be still. Nod your head.***)*

4. Was Marci thinking about the fire fighter's story? How could you tell?

   No. She was looking out the window daydreaming.

5. What do you think a good listener thinks about when the other person is talking?

   what the person is saying (Write **Think about what the speaker is saying.***)*

6. What could the students do to find out more from the fire fighter?

   ask questions (Write **Ask questions.***)*

Social Skills Activities

Skill A

Look at the Speaker

1. Show students what you mean by eye contact. Try the "looking game." Have a student sit a few feet away from another student. Have them look in each others' eyes. Then see who looks away first. Time your students and tell them how long they looked at each other.

2. Another way to emphasize good eye contact is to let your students experience how it feels to try to talk to people who aren't looking at them. Ask a student a question. When he answers, gaze out the window, play with your pencil, or begin writing a note. Ask him to describe how it feels to talk to someone who doesn't seem to be listening.

Skill B

Be Still

1. Some students may say they're able to listen while they're doing other things. While this might be true, the speaker may not think these students are listening. Students need to show the speaker that they are listening. They can do this by keeping their bodies still.

   Have students contrast still bodies and active bodies. Encourage a relaxed listening stance. Then, let your students name the body parts that need to remain still. *hands, mouth, feet*

Skill C

Nod Your Head

1. To listen, not just hear, your students must pay attention. The behavior of the good listener says to the speaker, "Tell me more." Nodding, smiling, and saying things like, "yes," "uh-huh," "oh, I see" are a few responses that encourage the other person to keep on speaking. Students should learn that looking away or not making responses discourages the speaker.

   Divide your class into pairs. Have one student talk about something exciting that happened to him. Have the other student look away and say nothing as the speaker talks. Talk about how the speaker feels when his partner looks away.

Skill D

Think About What the Speaker is Saying

1. A good listener sets aside her own thoughts to pay attention to the speaker's thoughts.

   Have your students find partners. Have one student in each pair be the speaker and her partner be the listener. Ask the speaker to tell the listener something about herself. Ask the listeners to tell what they thought about while they listened to the speakers. Then, have the partners switch roles and repeat the activity. Ask your students:

   "What makes listening to someone hard?"

   "What makes listening to someone easy?"

Skill E

Ask Questions

1. Good listening helps you understand someone. Asking questions increases that understanding. Questions can be used to gain more information or to clarify the message.

   Give students sample sentences. Have them ask questions about each sentence. For example, you could say, "We'll be talking about something fun today." Then, ask your students what questions they could ask you. They may ask:

   "What will we be talking about?"

   "Why is it fun?"

Other sentences you can say are:

"I wish my dad lived closer."

"I'm making a great supper tonight."

"You'll love what I have planned for you next week!"

"I can't wait until tomorrow!"

Additional Activities

Role-Playing

Review the story in this lesson. Then, select one or both of the following role-play activities.

Choose volunteers to play Bonnie's dad and Marci. Pretend that Bonnie's dad is explaining how the mask and the air pack protected him from breathing the smoke. Marci is listening to his story. Remind the person playing Marci to show the fire fighter that she is listening.

Choose volunteers to play Chee and Mark. Pretend that Chee is telling Mark about a television show he missed last night. Remind the person playing Mark to use good listening skills.

Role-Play Feedback

Encourage the rest of your students to give helpful feedback to the role-play volunteers. Use the following questions:

What did you like about each character's part?

What skills did Marci use to show she was listening?

What skills did Mark use to show he was listening?

How could the role plays be different?

Expanding Learning

Use pages 32 and 33 in the Activities Book to help your students distinguish between good and poor listening.

Use pages 70 through 77 in the Picture Book to help your students improve skills for listening by

- showing the speaker that they're listening
- putting away distracting objects in order to pay attention
- avoiding distracting noises that may keep them from listening

Use page 34 in the Activities Book to help your students review the skills learned for being a good listener. Have your students suggest when and how they can practice these skills. For example, they may say

"I will look at my teacher."

"I will keep my feet still."

"I will nod when she is teaching math."

"I will think about math."

"I will ask my teacher how she got the answer to problem two."

Visualization

Have your students get in comfortable positions to relax. Then say, "Close your eyes and imagine yourself being a good listener.

"You're sitting with your friend on a soft carpet in a quiet room. Your friend is telling you about his plane trip. You're facing your friend and your hands and feet are still. You're thinking about the things he tells you and nodding your head. Now you're asking a question about the plane trip to find out more. Imagine your friend enjoying talking with you. You're both smiling because you're having a good time talking with each other. When it's time to say good-bye, you tell your friend you'll see him tomorrow. You feel good as you walk away because you showed your friend you were listening."

Lesson 2: Asking for Help

Skills

A. Try on your own first.

B. Decide what help you need.

C. Raise your hand.

D. Ask politely.

Materials

Activities Book:
pages 35 through 37

Picture Book:
pages 78 through 85

Introduction

Some students miss learning opportunities because they're afraid asking for help will make them look stupid.

Other students might not request help in an appropriate tone of voice. They may demand rather than ask. People don't appreciate demands. Teachers respond more willingly to pleasant requests.

It's important for your students to learn to ask questions to interact appropriately with their teachers in the classroom. Students who can ask for help appropriately are seen as responsible learners.

Goals

In this lesson, your students will increase their classroom responsibility by learning when and how to ask for help. The activities will teach your students to

- try to find the answer by themselves first
- be specific when asking for help
- raise their hands and wait patiently until someone can help
- ask in a friendly tone of voice
- learn to ask the right person for help at the right time
- listen when help is given
- say thank you

Preparation

Talk to your students about the importance of asking for help if they need it. Fill a bag so full of books that you have to carry it in both hands. Carry the filled bag and walk to the closed classroom door and try to open it. Show your students that you're having trouble opening the door and ask one of them for help. Then, talk to your students about what could have happened if you hadn't asked for help.

Social Skills Story

Use page 78 in the Picture Book for this story. Ask, "Can you think of a time when you didn't ask for help when you should have? Tell about it. One day, Jonathan asked for help. But he didn't ask politely. Listen to this story."

It was Jonathan's first day back at school after being sick for a week. He was glad to be with his friends again.

But Jonathan felt confused on his first day back. He had missed some things the class had studied. He needed help from his teacher to catch up.

Jonathan raised his hand and waited until Mrs. Sahwani could help him each time he asked for help. She seemed glad to help, but he kept having trouble doing his work. After a while, Jonathan thought he looked stupid raising his hand.

Then, after lunch, Mrs. Sahwani gave each student a picture of a truck, a car, a banana, a peach, and a motorcycle. Jonathan heard Mrs. Sahwani say, "Categorize your pictures." Jonathan sat at his desk and stared at them. He saw other students quickly moving their pictures around, but he didn't understand what to do.

Without thinking, Jonathan blurted, "Huh? You've got to be kidding!"

Mrs. Sahwani looked surprised at Jonathan's outburst.

Questions for Discussion

Say, "Let's talk about Jonathan's trouble at school and make a list of skills to remember when asking for help in the classroom." Write the skills on the chalkboard or a flip chart as your students respond.

1. While Jonathan was absent, the class learned that categorizing is putting the same kinds of objects into groups. What do you think Jonathan could have asked to get the help he needed?

   What does categorize *mean?*

2. What classroom social skill did Jonathan need to practice?

   how to ask for help

3. How did Jonathan feel when he kept having trouble?

   He felt stupid.

4. True or false? You should try on your own first before you ask for help.

   true (Write **Try on your own first.***)*

5. Do you think Mrs. Sahwani knew what help Jonathan needed? Why?

   No. He just said, "Huh?" (Write **Decide what help you need.***)*

6. Show what students should do to signal to their teachers they need help.

   students raise their hands (Write **Raise your hand.***)*

7. What is wrong with saying, "Huh? You've got to be kidding!"

   It's not polite. It doesn't tell the teacher what part you don't understand. (Write **Ask politely.***)*

8. After receiving help, what can you say to let your teacher know you're glad she helped you?

   Thank you.

Social Skills Activities

Skill A

Try on Your Own First

1. Say, "A caterpillar is independent. It searches for food on its own to take care of itself. When you try first before you ask for help, you're independent, too."

   Have your students make Independent Caterpillars. You'll need 5 x 8 cards entitled "Independent Caterpillar" and one-inch colored circles. Give each student a card and have her draw a simple head for her caterpillar on the left side of the card. She will collect a colored circle to glue on her caterpillar to make its body each time she tries first before asking a question. After her caterpillar's body has six parts, have her draw its antennae and hang it on a bulletin board.

2. Sing these words to the tune of "If You're Happy and You Know It, Clap Your Hands."

   If you tried first and you did it,
   Clap your hands.

   If you tried first and you did it,
   Clap your hands.

   If you tried first and you did it,
   You're an Independent Learner.

   If you tried first and you did it,
   Clap your hands.

3. Tell your students there are times when they may need to ask for help immediately. At those times, it isn't appropriate to wait. Brainstorm such times. Your students might name these situations: a worksheet is torn, print is too light to read, something has gone wrong such as spilled paint in art class, someone continues to bother you and you need to move to another desk.

Skill B

Decide What Help You Need

Help your students use questions productively. Emphasize that specific questions tell teachers what help you need.

1. Say, "Listen to these requests for help. Show thumbs-up if the request tells exactly what is needed. Show thumbs-down if the request doesn't tell what help is needed."

   "Huh?" *down*

   "Should we use pencils or pens?" *up*

   "You've gotta be kidding!" *down*

   "I don't understand." *down*

   "I've finished the first math problem, but I don't understand the first sentence in problem two." *up*

   "I looked for this word in two places in the dictionary. I can't think of another way to spell it." *up*

2. With your older students, discuss ways to ask for help during tests. Ask your students why it's important to be careful about the kinds of questions they ask during tests. Help them word questions that won't reveal answers.

Skill C

Raise Your Hand

1. Point out that raising your hand is appropriate in the classroom, music, or art class, but not necessary at home or with friends.

   Discuss the need to wait until help can be given. Have your students practice raising their hands and saying the sentence, "I can wait without talking," in each of the following situations:

You're reading a library book. You've come to a long word you don't know. The librarian is walking around the room helping various students. You raise your hand and say to yourself, "I can wait without talking."

You can't read the third word on the chalkboard because the flowers on your teacher's desk are in the way. You raise your hand and say to yourself, "I can wait without talking."

Skill D

Ask Politely

1. Read these requests for help. Then, have your students judge whether you used an impolite or friendly tone of voice. Later, have various students practice these sentences, using a friendly tone of voice:

   "Explain again how to use the black construction paper in our pictures." (Use a demanding tone of voice.)

   "I'm having trouble cutting out the clouds for my picture. Will you please help me?" (Use a friendly tone.)

   "I've tried to work the math problem, but I don't understand how to do it." (Use an impatient, disgusted tone of voice.)

   "I'm ready to go home, but I can't find my blue mitten." (Use a friendly tone of voice.)

2. Provide a large mirror. Discuss how your students' bodies express friendliness or impoliteness. In front of the mirror, have them practice the sentences in number one.

3. If you have a video camera, tape your students as they practice asking for help. Then, as they view themselves, point out the various ways that body language sends messages. Have students check the following aspects of nonverbal communication:

   facial expression

   posture

   gestures

   As your students practice asking for help, have them judge their requests for help with this question: Would my teacher be pleased to help me? Why?

4. Ask your students whether or not it would be polite to ask for help with a math problem during the following times:

   Your teacher is talking with the principal. *no*

   Your teacher has just asked, "Are there any questions?" *yes*

   Your teacher is helping another student. *no*

   The announcements are being given on the loudspeaker. *no*

   Your class is having a fire drill. *no*

   Your teacher is walking around the room. *yes*

Additional Activities

Role-Playing

Review the story in this lesson. Then, select one or both of the following role-play activities.

Choose volunteers to play Jonathan and Mrs. Sahwani. Pretend that Jonathan tries to figure out what *categorize* means on his own first. Then, if he needs help he will ask

Mrs. Sahwani. Remind the student playing Jonathan to use the skills for asking for help.

Choose volunteers to play a student, a teacher, and a principal. Pretend the teacher has asked the student to change the classroom calendar. The student tries to reach the hook that holds the calendar, but it's too high. It's against the classroom rules to stand on chairs. The teacher is standing at the classroom door talking with the principal. Remind the person playing the student to use the skills for asking for help.

Role-Play Feedback

Encourage the rest of your students to give helpful feedback to the role-play volunteers. Use the following questions:

What did you like about each character's part?

Did Jonathan use all the skills for asking for help?

What did the student do to show politeness?

How could these role plays be different?

Expanding Learning

Use pages 35 and 36 in the Activities Book to help your students learn more about

- trying on their own before asking for help
- asking in a friendly way

Use pages 78 through 85 in the Picture Book to help your students improve skills in asking for help by

- accepting responsibility for learning
- interacting appropriately with teachers

Use page 37 in the Activities Book to help your students review the skills learned in asking for help. Have your students suggest when and how they can practice these skills. For example, a student may say

"I will try to sound out a word on my own."

"I need help reading a word."

"I will raise my hand for the librarian."

"I will sound friendly."

Visualization

Have your students get in comfortable positions to relax. Then say, "Close your eyes and imagine that you know how to ask for help at school.

"You're seated at your desk. Your reading book is in front of you. The teacher is saying, 'Read the story on pages 21-23 silently. Then we'll talk about the story.' You read page 21 and turn the page. To your surprise, page 23 has been ripped out of your book. You look around the room for your teacher. She is doing work at her desk. You raise your hand and wait. You tell yourself, 'I know I can wait.'

"In a moment, your teacher sees you and comes quietly to your desk. In a soft voice, so you won't disturb the other students, you say, 'The last page in my story has been torn out.' Your teacher smiles and gives you another book. You say, 'Thank you.' You open the new book and continue reading. You are glad you know how to ask for help at school."

Lesson 3: Saying Thank You

Skills

A. Ask yourself, "Should I say thank you?"

B. Choose a good time.

C. Be sincere and friendly.

Materials

Activities Book:
pages 38 through 40

Picture Book:
pages 86 through 93

Introduction

Some of your students have never been taught to say thank you. Others have been taught, but haven't formed a habit of being thankful. They don't say thank you at school unless they're reminded. Some students don't say thank you because they choose to use bad manners as a way of getting attention. These students need to learn the benefits of positive attention and the admiration of peers and adults.

Learning to say thank you is an important step in using good manners at school. Your students can learn that polite behavior can help smooth everyday life at school.

Goals

In this lesson, your students will learn that saying thank you is a way to show appreciation to others for any considerate actions. It's a way to show caring and a way to make life at school run a little more smoothly. The activities in this lesson will help teach your students to

- make saying thank you a habit
- say thank you sincerely
- understand why it's important to say thank you

Preparation

Encourage thoughtfulness in your classroom. Ask your students why they think it's important to say thank you. Point out that saying thank you is a polite habit. It'll help others to like your students better.

Talk about the meanings of the words *thankful*, *considerate*, and *sincere*. Explain that *thankful* means feeling good because of a favor you received. Point out that your students should say thank you when someone has helped them or given them something. Remind your students that they should always say thank you when someone gives them a present, whether they like it or not.

Explain that *considerate* means being thoughtful of others and their feelings. Saying thank you is a way to be considerate.

Explain that *sincere* means real and honest. Help your students express their thanks sincerely. Students can use positive body language to show that they really appreciate something. You may want to talk about nice things students can do to show their appreciation.

Social Skills Story

Use page 86 in the Picture Book with this story. Introduce the idea that saying thank you is a way of showing appreciation to another person. There aren't rules for how often to say thank you. But thank you is something people remember when you forget to say it! Ask, "Why do we say thank you?" Say, "Mrs. Sahwani's class had a good reason to say thank you one day at school. Listen to this story."

Everyone in Mrs. Sahwani's class felt excited one Friday morning. The class had won the Good Eaters' prize. This was the weekly prize for the class with the best lunchroom behavior. Each Friday, the principal, Mr. Walker, served pizza to the winning class.

"I'm proud of your good manners in the lunchroom," Mrs. Sahwani told the class. "Your good manners show that you care. That makes your friends want to sit next to you."

Mrs. Sahwani continued, "Good manners are nice habits that make you more well liked. Being polite is easy if you remember to treat others as you would like to be treated. But sometimes it's nice to know some tips for what to do."

José watched Mrs. Sahwani and wondered what she meant.

"I'll tell you a tip for today," she said. "Remember to say thank you when Mr. Walker serves us pizza. That way, he'll know we appreciate the trouble he's going to for us. After all, he doesn't have to give us pizza."

Then there was a knock at the classroom door. It was a sixth-grade student with a message that said Mr. Walker was ready for the class to come to the lunchroom. José felt excited as he got in line with his class to go to the lunchroom.

In the lunchroom, Mr. Walker smiled as the students sat down at a long table. Then he said, "It's important to be polite at school. You have won this Good Eaters' prize because you have used good manners in the lunchroom. I'm proud of you!"

When Mr. Walker served José's pizza, José smiled and sincerely said, "Thank you, Mr. Walker!" He saw a big grin on Mr. Walker's face.

"You're welcome, José," Mr. Walker replied.

Questions for Discussion

Say, "Let's talk about the story and make a list of skills for remembering to say thank you." Write the skills on the chalkboard or a flip chart as the students respond.

1. What social skill did José remember?

   saying thank you

2. Is it important to say thank you? Why?

   Yes. It shows that you appreciate what another person has done for you. (Write **Ask yourself, "Should I say thank you?"***)*

3. Did José choose a good time to thank Mr. Walker? Why is choosing a good time important?

   Yes. The other person can listen to you. (Write **Choose a good time.***)*

4. Do you think José really appreciated what Mr. Walker did for his class? How could you tell?

   Yes. He smiled; his voice sounded sincere. (Write **Be sincere and friendly.***)*

Social Skills Activities

Skill A

Ask Yourself, "Should I Say Thank You?"

1. Use puppets to help your students form the habit of saying thank you. Have your students make simple stick puppets from art sticks and circles cut from construction paper. Let the sticks form the bodies and the circles form the heads. Then, use the puppets to practice saying thank you in the situations below.

   Simple courtesies: Someone opened a door for you. Someone asked you to join a game. Someone asked you to come over. Someone picked up something you dropped.

   Compliments: Someone complimented your clothing, hair, or a picture you drew. Remind students that a simple thank you is more courteous than "Oh, I think I did a terrible job" or "This old dress?"

   Enjoyable times with others: You enjoyed a party, movie with a friend, or a good time playing ball. Remind students to thank their friends' parents, too, when they've visited a friend.

   When you've been served: Someone gave you food, drinks, or special help.

   Favors of any kind: Someone loaned you a pencil, gave you a ride home, or helped you with schoolwork. A favor deserves a word of thanks.

   Presents: Always say thank you, whether you liked the present or not! After all, it's the thought that counts.

Skill B

Choose a Good Time

1. Ask, "When is a good time to say thank you? Show thumbs-up if the time I say is a good time. Show thumbs-down if it's a bad time."

   Your good friend has handed you her favorite stuffed toy and said, "Want to play with it?" You take the toy and say thank you right away. *up*

   You go to your desk after recess and find that your teacher has put a smiley sticker on your spelling paper. You say thank you while she is talking to another teacher. *down*

   You dropped your pencil. Your friend picks it up and hands it to you. You smile and say, "Thanks, Mary." *up*

You forgot your lunch box, but your sister brings it to you in your classroom. After she leaves, you laugh and shout, "Thanks!" *down*

Skill C

Be Sincere and Friendly

1. Talk about the importance of positive body language when saying thank you. Say to your students, "Tell me *yes* when I say thank you in a sincere, friendly way and *no* when I don't seem sincere." After you role-play these situations, have student volunteers act out the same situations.

(smile sincerely) Thank you for the beautiful flowers! *yes*

(gush) This is a wonderful present. Oh, you shouldn't have gone to so much trouble. This is soooo great! How can I ever thank you? *no*

(look down as if someone made you say thank you) Well, thank you. *no*

(smile sincerely) It's wonderful that you remembered my birthday, Aunt Martha. Thank you! *yes*

Additional Activities

Role-Playing

Review the story in this lesson. Then, select one or both of the following role-play activities.

Choose volunteers to play José and Mr. Walker. Pretend Mr. Walker hands José a slice of pizza. Remind the person playing José to be sincere and friendly when he says thank you.

Choose volunteers to play Marci, Mrs. Sahwani, and Mrs. Nibling, the school secretary. Pretend Mrs. Sahwani has asked Marci to get a math book from the book room. When Marci tries to open the book room door, she finds out it is locked. The book room is next door to the school office where the secretary is working. Marci asks the secretary to unlock the door for her. Remind the person playing Marci to use all the skills for saying thank you.

Role-Play Feedback

Encourage the rest of your students to give helpful feedback to the role-play volunteers. Use the following questions:

What did you like about each character's part?

What skills for saying thank you did José use?

What skills for saying thank you did Marci use?

How could these role plays be different?

Expanding Learning

Use pages 38 and 39 in the Activities Book to help your students to learn more about

- occasions that call for you to say thank you
- how to be sincere when saying thank you

Use pages 86 through 93 in the Picture Book to help your students learn more about

- saying thank you in response to compliments
- remembering to say thank you
- avoiding insincere thank-yous

Use page 40 in the Activities Book to help your students review the skills learned for saying thank you. Have your students suggest when and how they can practice these skills. For example, a student may say.

> "I should say thank you when someone says, 'I like your jacket.' "
>
> "I will say thank you right after someone compliments my new jacket."
>
> "I will say thank you."

Visualization

Have your students get in comfortable positions to relax. Then say, "Imagine that you remembered to say thank you.

"You're on the school playground. You're running toward the slide. Just as you get to the slide steps, your friend arrives at the steps on the other side. You're both excited. But your friend steps back and says, 'You go first!' You understand that no one made your friend let you go first.

"You smile and say, 'Thanks! Let's go!' 'Ah, You're welcome,' says your friend with a smile. You and your friend go for a second turn. Then you say, 'You're first this time.' You're glad you know how to be polite and say thank you."

Lesson 4: Following Directions

Skills

A. Tune in to directions.

B. Wait to hear all the directions.

C. Ask a question if you don't understand.

D. Ask yourself, "What is my job?"

E. Ask yourself, "Am I doing my job?"

Materials

Activities Book:
pages 41 through 43

Picture Book:
pages 94 through 101

Introduction

Students must understand and follow directions in order to take in information. Teachers expect students to listen to their instructions, ask appropriate questions if necessary, and follow the directions.

Goals

In this lesson, your students will improve their skills for following directions. The activities will help your students

- learn to wait for all the directions before beginning a task
- repeat the directions to themselves
- determine if and when it's appropriate to ask a question
- check their work

Preparation

Think about your students' difficulties with following directions. Some students know how to follow directions, but they don't always follow them. Are these students purposefully ignoring directions? Are they daydreaming instead of listening? Are these students jumping into the actvity before they hear the complete directions?

Other students don't know how to follow directions. Are these students having trouble focusing on the directions? Do they give eye contact? What kind of body language do they show? Do these students understand the vocabulary of instruction? Is remembering the directions hard for them? Do they have trouble making the transition from their previous activity to the new one? These questions may help you to determine if your students need help for following directions.

Teachers and other adults must be careful not to overwhelm a child with long, unorganized sets of directions, especially oral directions. Ask yourself these questions about the next directions you give:

- Did I have the attention of students before I began?
- Did I speak clearly?
- Did I speak slowly and use pauses appropriately?
- Did I use short sentences?
- Did I present steps in a logical sequence?
- Did I use vocabulary and concepts students could understand?
- Did I adequately demonstrate new tasks?

Social Skills Story

Use page 94 in the Picture Book with this story. Ask your students, "Have you ever felt impatient when your teacher was explaining what she wanted you to do? How do you feel when you do your work wrong because you didn't follow the directions? Is following directions at school an important social skill we can work on?" Say, "Chee needed to learn more about following her teacher's directions. Listen to this story."

Chee felt excited one morning during art class. She could hardly stay in her chair. Mrs. Sahwani was showing the class a picture. "Today we will make pictures like this one by pouring some India ink on art paper and blowing on the ink gently through a drinking straw until it makes a design."

Chee looked at Mrs. Sahwani's unusual picture of swirling black ink and thought she could see puppies running in the wind. She tapped her fingers impatiently on the desk. "I'm sure I know how to make this picture," she thought. "I wish Mrs. Sahwani would finish talking so I can get started."

Mrs. Sahwani told students to spread newspaper on the tables and put their sheets of art paper on top of the newspaper. She had given each student a straw and a bottle of thick black India ink and said, "Listen to my directions before you begin your picture."

Chee had carefully placed her art paper, India ink bottle, and a drinking straw on the table just as her teacher had instructed. She watched Mrs. Sahwani as she began to explain how to make the picture.

But Chee didn't hear all the directions. She didn't hear her teacher warn, "Pour only a small amount of ink on your art paper. You must gently blow the ink to make your picture, like this." She didn't see Mrs. Sahwani show how to do it.

Chee thought she didn't need to listen. She was sure she knew how to make the picture. She quickly opened her bottle of ink. Before she knew it, she had poured half the bottle of ink onto her art paper. It was too much. The ink quickly ran off the table onto her new plaid jumper.

Questions for Discussion

Say, "Let's talk about the story and make a list of skills Chee can follow next time she has to follow directions." Write the skills on the chalkboard or a flip chart as your students respond.

1. What social skill does Chee need to learn?

   how to follow directions

2. What is the most important thing to remember when following directions?

   Listen to them. (Write **Tune in to directions.***)*

3. Why did Chee have a problem following directions?

   She didn't wait to hear all of the directions. (Write **Wait to hear all the directions.***)*

4. If you have tried to listen carefully and still don't understand directions, what should you do?

   Ask a question. (Write **Ask a question if you don't understand.***)*

5. What could you do to be sure you are following directions?

   Repeat the directions; answers will vary. (Write **Ask yourself, "What is my job?"***)*

6. If you understand the directions, how can you check yourself to see if you're doing the task?

   Ask yourself if you're doing it. (Write **Ask yourself, "Am I doing my job?"***)*

Social Skills Activities

Skill A

Tune In to Directions

1. Use a radio to demonstrate the importance of tuning in. Contrast the clear message received when the station is tuned in clearly with the noise received when the dial is off the mark. Say, "A message is sent from a radio station. You don't hear it, however, unless you tune in by moving the dial. When listening to directions, you won't get the message unless you tune in by paying attention. Paying attention means watching, listening, and trying to understand the message."

2. Assign every student a study buddy. Pair a good listener who generally follows directions well with a student who's having difficulty following directions. Let the students check their directions with their partners.

Skill B

Wait to Hear All the Directions

1. Give long directions to a student before you say the student's name. The student will probably have difficulty answering because he wasn't sure you were giving the directions to him. This activity should encourage your students to listen until the end of your directions.

2. Ask students to list why it's important to wait until they hear all the directions before they begin a task. Discuss reasons some students might believe they don't have to wait until the teacher finishes giving directions before they begin.

Skill C
Ask a Question if You Don't Understand

1. Discuss the importance of asking a question if you don't understand. List situations that require a question:

   tried to understand, but feel confused

   didn't understand some of the vocabulary

   didn't hear because of distracting noise

Skill D
Ask Yourself, "What Is My Job?"

1. Discuss the importance of repeating the directions after the teacher gives them. Ask, "Why is it important to tell yourself the directions before you begin?"

2. Play a game, such as "Simon Says," and ask students to repeat the directions before they do the action. Spot check from time to time when you have given some particularly difficult directions by having students repeat the directions out loud.

3. Give simple directions to your students just for fun. Ask students to repeat the directions each time before they begin.

   Go to the classroom door, open it, then go to my desk chair and sit down, Sandra.

   Tap your desk with your pencil, turn your head, and cough, Jackie.

   Wink your eyes, wave your hand, and point to the window, Michelle.

   Tell your birthday, your address, and your favorite food, Dan.

Skill E
Ask Yourself, "Am I Doing My Job?"

1. Encourage independent work habits by developing checklists or models when you're teaching new routine skills, such as writing the heading on your students' papers. Place a model of the expected heading on the chalkboard or an overhead. Then, students can check to see if they have followed directions.

Additional Activities

Role-Playing

Review the story in this lesson. Then, select one or both of the following role-play activities.

Choose volunteers to play Chee and Mrs. Sahwani. Pretend that Mrs. Sahwani gives short and clear directions about making the ink picture. Pretend that Chee follows Mrs. Sahwani's directions. Remind the student playing Chee to use the skills for following directions.

Choose volunteers to play a teacher and a student. Pretend the teacher is telling the student the following directions: "It's time to prepare for lunch. Put your worksheets in the left corner tray on my desk, get your lunch boxes, and line up at the door." Remind the student to use the skills for following directions.

Role-Play Feedback

Encourage the rest of your students to give helpful feedback to the role-play volunteers. Use the following questions:

What did you like about each character's part?

What skills did Chee use for following directions?

What skills did the student use for following directions?

How could these role plays be different?

Expanding Learning

Use pages 41 and 42 in the Activities Book to help your students

- learn more about how watching and listening can help them tune in to directions

Use pages 94 through 101 in the Picture Book to help your students improve skills in following directions by

- listening in order to tune in to directions
- practicing control instead of jumping in before teachers have finished giving directions

Use page 43 in the Activities Book to help your students review the skills in following directions. Have your students suggest when and how they can practice these skills. For example, they might say

"I will look at my art teacher."

"I will listen to all of her directions on Monday."

"I will ask my art teacher if I don't understand."

"I will repeat my art teacher's directions to myself."

"I'm doing my art work."

Visualization

Have your students get in comfortable positions to relax. Then say, "Close your eyes and imagine that you know how to follow directions at school.

"You're seated at your desk looking at a worksheet about tools. Your teacher begins to give directions. So you sit still, look at your teacher, and try to understand all of the directions.

"She says, 'Write your name in the upper right corner of your paper. Then, circle all the gardener's tools, but underline the painter's tools.' When she finishes giving directions, you look at your worksheet and say to yourself, 'My name goes at the top of the right side of the page. I must circle the tools a gardener uses and underline the tools a painter uses.'

"You don't need to ask a question because you understand what to do. As you work, you ask yourself, 'Am I following all the directions?' You check your name, the underlined tools, and the circled tools. You know you have followed your teacher's directions well."

Lesson 5: Asking Questions

Skills

A. What question do you need to ask?

B. Who should you ask?

C. When should you ask your question?

D. Ask in a friendly way.

E. Say thank you.

Materials

Activities Book:
pages 44 through 46

Picture Book:
pages 102 through 109

Introduction

Students who ask unnecessary questions need to learn that too many questions are irritating. These students must learn to listen carefully and find information independently.

Some students might not ask questions when they should. These students might not recognize they need to know certain information. There are also students who are afraid they'll be laughed at or yelled at if they ask questions. These students might not understand who, what, where, when, how, and why to ask questions.

Goals

In this lesson, your students will improve skills for asking questions. The activities will help your students to

- ask questions as a learning technique
- use questions to reason
- use questions to gain information
- use questions to solve problems
- learn appropriate times and places to ask questions
- learn how to ask questions

Preparation

Create an atmosphere in your classroom that allows time for your students to ask questions. Let your students know that you expect questions. Tell them that asking questions is a part of learning.

Discuss examples of questions using who, what, where, when, why, and how. Explain differences between *questions* and *demands*. Tell students that a question asks but a demand tells. Demonstrate the difference between "Give me the pencil" and "Could you please hand me the pencil?"

Stress ways your students can be courteous while asking questions through their tone of voice and using polite words, such as please and thank you. Discuss why it's important to say thank you once questions have been answered. Demonstrate how body language conveys politeness through smiles, open posture, and pleasant expressions.

Social Skills Story

Use page 102 in the Picture Book with this story. Introduce the idea that questions are a good tool for gaining information. Say, "Has someone ever helped you figure out the answer to a problem? How did the person know you needed the information? Did you ask a question? Is asking questions to solve problems something you need to work on? Bonnie did. Listen to this story."

Bonnie frowned as she read the sign on the school nurse's door: Do Not Disturb. "That means don't bother the people inside," Bonnie told herself.

So she didn't knock on the door. Instead, she quietly walked back to her classroom.

One hour later, Bonnie came back and the sign was still there. She rubbed her forehead. "I've got to get into the office before lunch hour to get my lunch. What will I do?" she thought. Earlier, Bonnie had left her lunch on the nurse's desk while the nurse put a Band-Aid on her scratched knee.

"I need to ask someone when the nurse's office will be empty," Bonnie thought. "I can't wait much longer because it's almost lunchtime."

Bonnie looked around. No one was in the hallway. Then, she heard voices next door. It was Mrs. Nibling, the secretary, talking with Mr. Walker, the principal, and Mr. Lenski, the music teacher.

Bonnie felt hopeful. "Maybe Mrs. Nibling can help me," she thought. She ran into the principal's office. "Get my lunch out of the nurse's office quick. I gotta eat," Bonnie said.

Questions for Discussion

Say, "Let's talk about the skills Bonnie could use next time to get information that will help her." Write the skills on the chalkboard or a flip chart as your students respond.

1. What was Bonnie's problem?

   She needed to get her lunch.

2. Did Bonnie need to ask a question? Why?

   Yes. She needed to get her lunch.

3. What question did Bonnie need to ask?

   When can I go into the nurse's office to get my lunch? (Write **What question do you need to ask?***)*

4. Do you think there was any other way Bonnie could have found out when she could get into the office?

   Answers will vary.

5. What do you think Bonnie needs to tell the secretary before she asks her question? Why?

   She left her lunch in the nurse's office and needs it before lunch hour. The secretary didn't know about her problem.

6. What question do you need to ask yourself when deciding who to ask?

   Who should I ask? (Write **Who should you ask?***)*

7. Bonnie interrupted the secretary, the principal, and the music teacher. Explain how Bonnie could have chosen a good time to ask her question.

   She could have waited until they stopped talking. She could have said, "Excuse me."

8. What question do you need to ask yourself when deciding when to ask your question?

   When should I ask? (Write **When should you ask your question?***)*

9. It's best to ask a question in a friendly way. Which of these would show friendly ways: Biting your nails? Frowning? Smiling? Stamping your foot? Crying? A nice tone of voice?

   smiling, nice tone of voice (Write **Ask in a friendly way.***)*

10. Pretend that Bonnie asked the secretary in a friendly way to get her lunch. What could Bonnie have said to the secretary after she got her lunch?

    (Write **Say thank you.***)*

Social Skills Activities

Skill A

What Question Do You Need to Ask?

1. Point out opportunities to ask responsible questions in various school settings. Talk about ways your students can get the person's attention before asking the question, such as raising their hands, making eye contact, or saying the person's name. Talk about how asking a question in an emergency is different from asking a routine question.

2. Guide your students to decide whether they need to ask a question or find the answer themselves. Talk about when it may be appropriate to look up information in a book instead of asking a question. Ask your students to tell the best source of information in these situations:

   You're making up a puppet show about a story in your reading book, but you forgot the main character's name. *Look in the book.*

You forgot the page number your teacher told you to turn to and you're sitting close to your friend. *Look at the page number your friend turned to.*

Everyone in art class has a paintbrush except you. *Ask your art teacher for a paintbrush.*

Your friend borrowed your crayons yesterday. Now you need them to draw a picture. *Ask your friend to return your crayons.*

You're at school, but you need to call your mom at work. You forgot her work phone number. *Look in the telephone book.*

You found a mitten outside your classroom door. You wonder if it belongs to someone in your class. *Ask your classmates.*

Now, help your students formulate questions for the situations that involve asking people questions.

3. Point out to your students that questions can help them get missing information. Omit some needed information from your instructions for a game or a task. For example, give your students instructions for an art project, but omit an important step. Or, give permission to play a game that requires a ball, but leave the ball inside.

Skill B
Who Should You Ask?

1. Have your students name the person who would be the best at answering the following questions:

   "What day does our class go on its field trip?" The teacher or a classmate? *teacher*

   "When can I get my hair cut?" Your mom or the school secretary? *your mom*

   "When will we eat?" Your dad or your younger sister? *your dad*

   "Will you reach the cereal box for me?" Your tall uncle or your baby brother? *your tall uncle*

   "Will you help me with question four?" Your teacher or the mail carrier? *your teacher*

Skill C
When Should You Ask Your Question?

1. Discuss appropriate times to ask questions. Point out that times when a person is working on another task or talking to another person are poor times to ask a question. Point out that others are more likely to give information when they're asked at a good time and place.

   Have your students brainstorm good times and places to ask the following people the following questions:

   Teacher: How do you do problem six?

   Parent: May I go to José's party?

   Grandparent: Will you take me to the park?

   Parent: May I have some money?

   Sister: Will you read me a story?

Skill D
Ask in a Friendly Way

1. Practice understanding body language. Have volunteers demonstrate the body language below while asking the question, "When may I turn in my homework?" Ask other students to tell what message the expressions, gestures, or body movements might be giving.

   frowning
   rubbing your nose
   tilting your head
   biting your nails
   looking down at your feet
   smiling in a friendly way
   crossing your arms
   tapping your fingers

2. Discuss the difference between asking and demanding. Explain that asking in friendly ways helps your students get along with people, while demanding that people do things might turn others away. Ask your students to change these demands into friendly requests:

   Get my crayons. They fell on the floor. *Will you please hand me my crayons?*

   Tell me what page. I didn't hear you. *Could you please repeat the page number?*

   Give me a cupcake. *May I have a cupcake?*

   Show me how to do the second problem. *Will you please explain the second problem to me?*

Skill E

Say Thank You

1. Have students wrap objects in newspaper or gift wrap. Divide students into pairs. Give each student a wrapped package. Have the children take turns giving their packages to each other. Tell your students to say thank you after they open the packages.

2. Say *yes* or *no* to the following times you should say thank you:

   when a friend's mom drives you home from school *yes*

   your grandpa buys you an ice-cream cone *yes*

   your friend borrows your bike *no*

   your dog chews on your new shoes *no*

   your friend picks up your pencil you dropped *yes*

   you give a friend a present *no*

Additional Activities

Role-Playing

Review the story in this lesson. Then, select one or both of the following role-play activities.

Choose volunteers to play Bonnie and Mrs. Nibling, the secretary. Pretend that Bonnie asks Mrs. Nibling when the nurse's office will be empty. Remind the student playing Bonnie to ask her question at the right time.

Choose volunteers to play a student and a teacher. Pretend that the teacher has given everyone three pages of math homework. When this student checks his pages, he finds that there has been a mistake. Each of his pages has the same problems. He wants to ask a question, but his teacher has her back turned while she is writing on the chalkboard. Remind the person playing the student to use the skills for asking a question.

Role-Play Feedback

Encourage the rest of your students to give helpful feedback to the role-play volunteers. Use the following questions:

What did you like about each character's part?

What skills did Bonnie use for asking questions?

What skills did the student use for asking questions?

How could these role plays be different?

Expanding Learning

Use pages 44 and 45 in the Activities Book to help your students

- formulate questions to get information
- request instead of demand

Use pages 102 through 109 in the Picture Book to help your students improve skills for asking questions by

- learning more about responsible use of questions to solve problems and get information at school
- helping your students begin to see that people can be important sources of information
- learning that questions can be used in responsible ways to tap information

Use page 46 in the Activities Book to help your students review the skills learned in asking questions. Have your students suggest when and how they can practice these skills. For example, they may say

"I need to ask if Jenna can help me with my math homework."

"I will ask Jenna."

"I will ask Jenna during recess."

"I will say, 'Jenna, will you please help me with my math homework?' "

"I will say, 'Thank you.' "

Visualization

Have your students get in comfortable positions to relax. Then say, "Close your eyes and imagine that you know how to ask a question to find out things.

"You're on the playground watching three friends who are playing a game. It looks like fun. You'd like to play, too, but you don't know the rules. You see that they're almost finished with the first round. So you wait until they're done. In a friendly voice you say, 'Hey Scott, that looks like fun. Will you show me how to play?' Scott says, 'Sure, come on. We'll show you. It's not hard.' You're glad you asked a question. You learned a fun new game."

Lesson 6: Taking Part in Discussions

Skills

A. Listen and think about the topic.

B. Raise your hand if you want the teacher to call on you.

C. Stay on the topic.

D. Let others talk, too.

Materials

Activities Book:
pages 47 through 49

Picture Book:
pages 110 through 117

Introduction

Students need to learn the characteristics of a good classroom discussion. Some students bore others by monopolizing conversations. Some students who don't know how to get to the point in a conversation can ruin a group discussion. Getting off the topic is another way to block a good discussion. Not listening, not joining in, and not speaking discourage good discussions. When students whisper, interrupt, argue, and put down others, they stop productive discussion periods. These students need to understand that their negative behaviors may ruin opportunities for learning.

The people involved in a good classroom discussion take turns being listeners and speakers. They all pay attention to the topic. A good discussion includes speaking clearly, listening carefully, and asking questions when necessary to understand the information. To keep the discussion going, a speaker uses good expression and watches the listeners' reactions. With practice and your guidance, your students can learn to join in or take part in good discussions.

Goals

In this lesson, your students will improve skills for taking part in classroom discussions. The activities will help your students learn to

- contribute to discussions
- learn from others during discussions
- listen to speakers
- stay on the topic
- make their comments brief and to the point
- know when it's important to raise their hands for permission to talk

Preparation

Encourage your students to respect their own ideas as well as the ideas others may share during discussions. Tell your students that *discuss* means to talk. Explain that the *topic* is the main idea under discussion.

Emphasize to your students that teachers expect students to have good classroom discussion skills. Ask your students why it's important to take part in classroom discussions. Point out that expressing their own ideas and listening to what others think can be an excellent way to learn.

Contrast good and poor discussions. Ask, "What are some ways that students can ruin a discussion?" Refusing to join in, failing to listen, getting off the topic, hogging the conversation, talking too loudly or softly, whispering, interrupting, or arguing can end a discussion. In successful discussions, students will listen, raise their hands, stay on topic, and take turns.

Social Skills Story

Use page 110 in the Picture Book with this story. Introduce the idea that joining in classroom discussion is an important way to learn at school. Say, "See if you can tell what's wrong with the discussion in Mrs. Sahwani's class today. Listen to this story."

Mrs. Sahwani said, "Our health lesson today is about exercise. Do you think kickball is a good way to get exercise at school?"

"Yuck," thought Mark. "I like baseball better." But he saw several students smiling and nodding their heads.

"Everyone, no matter how old, needs to skate, run, or do something to get exercise. Let's talk about exercise." Then, Mrs. Sahwani asked, "What's your favorite way to exercise?"

Mark blurted, "I like playing baseball at Carter Park with my Little League team. Man, you get these real good grape and strawberry snow cones there. My grandmother makes strawberry milk shakes. Yum, they're great!"

Mrs. Sahwani looked confused. She said, "Well, that does sound like something good to eat. But let's stay on the topic of exercise. What's your favorite way to exercise?"

Chee said loudly, "I love to exercise, Mrs. Sahwani. I jog with Grandfather. He has to exercise because he had a heart attack and the doctor makes him jog once a day. He even jogs when it's raining!"

Chee rushed on, "He likes me to jog with him. We're trying to jog farther every week. When you jog, it makes your heart beat faster and that's good for your heart. Grandmother doesn't jog with us, but she plays tennis. That's good exercise too."

Chee paused. She was out of breath.

Meanwhile, José had been staring out the window thinking about lunch. He whispered to Marci. "I'm getting hungry. Are you going through the hot lunch line today?"

All Mrs. Sahwani could do was shake her head. "Class, this discussion makes one thing clear about exercise. We need to exercise some classroom discussion skills," she said.

Questions for Discussion

Say, "Mrs. Sahwani was right. The class needed to work on classroom discussion skills. Some students didn't pay attention, raise their hands, or stay on the subject of exercise. Chee hogged the discussion. Let's make a list of skills to help the class have better discussions." Write the skills on the chalkboard or a flip chart as your students respond.

1. The first thing to remember about discussions is to listen and think about the subject the class is talking about. How did José break that rule?

   He stared out the window, thought about something else, and whispered to Marci. (Write **Listen and think about the topic.***)*

2. Why is listening and thinking about a discussion topic important?

   Answers will vary.

3. Did any of the students in the story raise their hands before talking?

   no

4. Why is it important to raise your hand during a classroom discussion?

   so the teacher can give students equal turns to talk (Write **Raise your hand if you want the teacher to call on you.***)*

5. Why was Mrs. Sahwani confused by Mark's story?

   Mark didn't stay on the topic. (Write **Stay on the topic.***)*

6. Chee stayed on the topic of exercise. But she hogged the discussion. How could she be better at taking part in discussions?

   She needs to say less. (Write **Let others talk, too.***)*

Social Skills Activities

Skill A

Listen and Think About the Topic

1. Point out that body language shows when someone is listening during a discussion. Say, "Show thumbs-up when I describe a good listening behavior. Show thumbs-down when I describe poor listening behavior."

   good eye contact *up*

   nodding your head *up*

   turning away from the other speakers *down*

   whispering to another student *down*

   rolling your eyes to show you don't agree with the speaker *down*

Skill B

Raise Your Hand if You Want the Teacher to Call on You

1. Ask your students to explain why it's important to raise their hands in classroom discussions. Then, compare times when it's important for them to raise their hands during a discussion and times when it's not necessary. Say, "Should you raise your hand in these situations?"

   A parent visits the classroom to tell about her work as a doctor. She asks for volunteers to tell what they know about hospitals. *yes*

   You're meeting with the principal and three other students in his office to discuss ways to improve hallway behavior. *no*

During lunch, you're discussing the class trip with two friends. *no*

Your teacher wants the class to decide how to give students more turns to paint at the classroom easel. *yes*

Skill C

Stay on the Topic

1. Discuss the importance of sticking to the topic. Say, "In a good discussion, each person stays on the subject until all the information has been shared. No one makes off-the-wall comments. Instead, everyone tries to keep the discussion going. Tell me which comments stick to the topic."

   Topic: Let's decide how we can have better behavior during fire drills.

   I hate fire drills. *no*

   We can stop talking as soon as we hear the alarm. *yes*

   We can walk instead of run when we go outside. *yes*

   Topic: Let's plan something special to do for Open House.

   We could make posters that welcome people to our room. *yes*

   Did you watch TV last night? *no*

   My mother let me buy a hamster. *no*

   Topic: How is second grade different from first grade?

   Students read more books in second grade. *yes*

   Math is harder in second grade. *yes*

   I'm buying hot lunch today. *no*

Skill D

Let Others Talk, Too

1. Tell your students that a good rule for keeping discussions interesting is to be brief. Explain that brief means a short time. For example, telling someone everything you can remember from a movie you saw is not being brief. Brief is telling about one small part, such as telling someone about one scene in the movie. Choose volunteers to talk about the following topics and have the other students tell if the speaker was brief.

   something you saw walking to school

   a TV show you watched

   a vacation you took

2. Everyone has been in a conversation or a discussion in which one person did all the talking. Ask, "How do you feel when one person talks too much?" Point out that sometimes other people may talk too much because they are nervous or worried about something.

3. Tell your students they can avoid being the speaker who hogs the conversation if they watch their listeners. Say, "Which body language says you might be talking too long?"

   Several people begin to yawn. *yes*

   Most people are watching you. *no*

   People begin to look away or look at their watches. *yes*

   Several people ask questions to find out more. *no*

   People begin to look bored. *yes*

Additional Activities

Role-Playing

Review the story in this lesson. Then, select one or both of the following role-play activities.

Choose volunteers to play Mrs. Sahwani and Mark. Pretend that Mrs. Sahwani wants the class to talk about ways to exercise. Pretend that Mark talks about his favorite way to exercise. Remind the person playing Mark to stick to the topic.

Choose volunteers to play Mrs. Sahwani, Bonnie, and Jonathan. Pretend that Mrs. Sahwani has finished reading a story that had a scary monster called Troll. She asks the class to tell the things that made Troll scary. Bonnie and Jonathan raise their hands and take part in the discussion. Remind the students playing Bonnie and Jonathan to use the skills for taking part in discussions.

Role-Play Feedback

Encourage the rest of your students to give helpful feedback to the role-play volunteers. Use the following questions:

> What did you like about each character's part?
>
> What skills for taking part in discussions did Mark use?
>
> What skills for taking part in discussions did Bonnie and Jonathan use?
>
> How could these role plays be different?

Expanding Learning

Use pages 47 and 48 in the Activities Book to help your students

- listen and raise their hands
- stay on the topic during discussions

Use pages 110 through 117 in the Picture Book to help your students improve their skills in taking part in discussions by

- staying on the topic
- being brief
- showing others they're listening
- speaking clearly when they're the speaker
- keeping a discussion going

Use page 49 in the Activities Book to help your students review the skills they have learned for taking part in discussions. Have your students suggest when and how they could practice these skills. For example, a student may say

> "I will listen and think about a discussion about classroom rules."
>
> "I will raise my hand when I want to talk."
>
> "I will talk about the classroom rules."
>
> "I will be brief."

Visualization

Have your students get in comfortable positions to relax. Then say, "Imagine that you sometimes feel shy about taking part in discussions. You're afraid someone will laugh at what you say. But you've decided to speak up today. Then your teacher says, 'We have a problem. Tori left her lunch on the school bus. The bus won't be back until school is out. And food won't be served at school today. Now, Tori won't have a lunch. How can we solve this problem?'

"You raise your hand. When the teacher calls on you, you say in a clear voice, 'We can share our lunches. That way, we would all have something to eat.' Someone says, 'That's a great idea.' Your teacher agrees. You feel glad that you spoke up during class. Next time, it'll be even easier."

Lesson 7: Finishing Your Work

Skills

A. Ask yourself, "Did I finish my work on time?"

B. Ask yourself, "Did I check my work?"

C. Ask yourself, "Did I hand it in?"

D. Tell yourself, "Great! I did it!"

Materials

Activities Book:
pages 50 through 52

Picture Book:
pages 118 through 125

Introduction

Incomplete assignments and papers with careless errors frustrate teachers and parents. Students become upset when they have to finish their work during recess or have to take it home.

Slow work habits have many causes. Students who find assignments too challenging may put off doing their work. Some students just prefer goofing off because they haven't learned the rewards that come from working. Other students have poor organizational skills.

Your students must learn to complete tasks to be successful at school. Teachers expect students to organize their time and materials so they can finish school assignments in the time allotted. Peers expect classmates to complete their work on time, too. What's more, students should expect themselves to complete their work on time.

Goals

In this lesson, your students will learn the skills for getting their schoolwork done on time. The activities will help your students

- learn the importance of getting started
- avoid distractions while working
- check their work for completeness, accuracy, and neatness
- know the rewards of task completion

Preparation

Create an atmosphere in your classroom that is orderly, cheerful, warm, and comfortable. Make it a place where both you and your students are able to enjoy working and learning.

Ask your students if they understand the assignments and when they're due. Ask them if they understand your expectations for work and the consequences for not doing work. Use rewards appropriately to encourage improvement.

Discuss the importance of taking responsibility for work by contrasting the meanings of the words *work* and *play*. First, point out that play helps students learn to work. Have your students recall some activities they played when they were younger, that are now work. For example, they used to play at writing letters. Now, they write to finish schoolwork.

Play includes the activities students do because they want to. Students play in response to their own wishes, desires, and wants.

Work refers to the activities that need to be done. To do their work, students might have to put off things they want to do until they finish what they need to do.

Ask, "What good things happen when you play? What good things happen when you work? What do you think about this statement, 'School can be more fun for students who choose to work when it's time to work and play when it's time to play.' "

Social Skills Story

Use page 118 in the Picture Book with this story. Introduce the idea that managing time is important in getting work finished on time. Say, "Have you ever had trouble getting your work finished? What was the problem? Why is it important to finish your work at school? One day Marci had trouble finishing her work. Listen to this story."

Marci sighed as she worked another math problem. The other students were having recess and the classroom was quiet. Marci felt alone, although Mrs. Sahwani was also working in the room. Marci thought, "Why was Mrs. Sahwani being so mean this morning?"

"Finishing work, phooey," thought Marci. It sure was boring working while everyone else was outside playing. She wanted to be with her friends. Why couldn't Mrs. Sahwani let her finish her math after recess? She thought about asking her teacher that question. Then, she remembered Mrs. Sahwani's words, "You may go to recess when you finish your work."

"Why am I having so much trouble getting finished today? I'm good at math," thought Marci.

Marci had to admit there was another problem. She could do the math, but she just couldn't seem to get started.

First, she had lost her pencil. When she had finally found it, she had to sharpen it. Then, Marci had stopped by Mrs. Sahwani's desk to show her the fancy eraser on her pencil.

After she'd finished the first problem, Marci had noticed a mistake. When she'd erased the numbers, Marci made a hole in her worksheet. She had to ask for another one.

By the time, Marci had started working again, Mrs. Sahwani had said, "It's time for recess. Check your math papers and hand them in."

Questions for Discussion

Say, "Now, let's talk about Marci's problem with getting finished. We'll try to think of some skills Marci can follow so that next time she'll finish on time." Write the skills on the chalkboard or a flip chart as your students respond.

1. What skill did Marci need to work on?

   finishing her math or finishing her work

2. Why didn't Marci finish her work on time?

   She didn't get started; she didn't have her materials ready.

3. When Marci was finally done, she looked at her work and asked herself, "Am I finished?" Why?

   to be sure she hadn't skipped a problem (Write **Ask yourself, "Did I finish my work on time?"***)*

4. Mrs. Sahwani reminded her students to check their work. What does *check your work* mean?

   Read each answer and ask yourself, it is correct? (Write **Ask yourself, "Did I check my work?"***)*

5. True or false? When Marci is done, she should put her paper in her book. Why?

   False. She should hand it in. (Write **Ask yourself, "Did I hand it in?"***)*

6. How do you think Marci felt when she finally finished her work and handed it in?

   Answers will vary.

7. Should another student who finished his work say, "Great. I've done a good job?" Why?

   Yes. He finished his work. (Write **Tell yourself, "Great! I did it!"***)*

8. Do you think Marci learned anything about finishing her work today?

   Answers will vary.

9. At first, Marci thought Mrs. Sahwani was mean. What do you think?

   Answers will vary.

Social Skills Activities

Skill A

Ask Yourself, "Did I Finish My Work on Time?"

1. Help your students learn to get started right away. Unless they do, they won't finish on time. Reinforce getting started in a fun way by making a "Busy Hands Tree." You will need green construction paper, pencils, scissors, and felt tip markers. Have each student make a hand by tracing around her own hand on the green construction paper and cutting it out. Collect the hands.

   Then, award a hand to each student who gets started right away. Students may write their names on the hands when they finish their work and pin the hands to the shape of a tree on a bulletin board. At the end of the period, lead your students in giving themselves a hand by clapping for those who got started right away.

2. Organizing materials is an important part of finishing work. Even young children can begin to organize their materials. Encourage your students to organize materials after you have introduced all the requirements and materials for an activity, like an art project. Allow your students to discuss what they'll need before they begin working. After the discussion, ask a

volunteer to list the items as you record them on a chalkboard. Students who are weak in organization skills can use the list as a checklist.

3. Organizing time is important for finishing work. Use a digital or kitchen timer to help your slower workers organize their time. When the task is assigned, set a kitchen timer for one minute. If everyone has begun the task when the bell rings, allow an additional two minutes of free time.

   Then, set the timer for five more minutes. If everyone is still on task, add two minutes more to the free time. Continue setting the timer for five minute allotments of time until your students are staying on task and finishing their work on time.

Skill B

Ask Yourself, "Did I Check My Work?"

1. To improve accuracy on assignments, play "Star Teams." Divide your students into two teams. Figure the team average percentage of accuracy on an assigned work. The team with the greatest accuracy becomes the Star Team of the Day. Each Star Team member wears a Star Team badge. The Star Team gets to choose a game for a special period of free time.

2. To improve neatness, state the specific criteria for neatness, like skipping lines between sentences. Post papers that meet the criteria on a bulletin board. Students can use them as reminders.

3. Reward improvements in a student's neatness by letting him be the class secretary. He can write your dictated messages to the principal and other teachers, comments of praise to your students, or complimentary notes to parents.

Skill C

Ask Yourself, "Did I Hand It in?"

1. Emphasize the importance of handing in work once it's finished. Lost homework and misplaced completed papers are not finished work. Point out that different teachers expect their students to hand in work in different ways. The music teacher, for example, may stand at the door and receive students' finished work, while the classroom teacher may expect her students to put their finished papers in a tray.

   Ask your students to list the various places that each of their teachers expects students to put finished work. Discuss the differences.

Skill D

Tell Yourself, "Great! I Did It!"

1. Explain that *pride* is the feeling you get when you finish a project. Suggest that when your students are proud, they may feel like walking a little taller. They may feel like smiling. Pride feels good. Have students role-play body language that shows they're feeling proud of finishing their work.

2. Tell your students that, as they grow up, they'll learn to reward themselves for doing a good job. Mention some ways that you reward yourself after a hard day at work.

Provide several activities that your students can choose as rewards for finishing their work. Here are some ideas:

watering the plants
using colored chalk
decorating the bulletin board
using a computer
stapling papers together
feeding the fish or the animals
giving a message over the intercom
picking up litter
taking the class roll
holding the door
serving as the secretary during meetings
listening to tapes at a listening station
sitting beside a friend
making a book
sharpening the teacher's pencils
sitting next to the teacher during lunch
writing with colored pencils
choosing a game to play

Additional Activities

Role-Playing

Review the story in this lesson. Then, select one or both of the following role-play activities.

Choose volunteers to play Mrs. Sahwani and Marci. Pretend that Marci gets to work right away and finishes on time. Pretend that Mrs. Sahwani is proud of Marci. Remind the person playing Marci to use the skills for finishing work.

Choose volunteers to play Jonathan, Mark, Mrs. Sahwani, and Mr. Walker. Pretend that Mrs. Sahwani told the students to write three sentences using their new spelling words. Then, Mr. Walker came to the door and talked quietly with Mrs. Sahwani. Jonathan and Mark did their work in different ways. At first, both boys got right to work. But Mark stopped working and watched the two adults. When Mr. Walker left, Mrs. Sahwani told the students to hand in their papers. Jonathan was finished with his work, but Mark wasn't. Show the way the two boys felt when it was time to hand in their work.

Role-Play Feedback

Encourage the rest of your students to give helpful feedback to the role-play volunteers. Use the following questions:

What did you like about each character's part?

What skills did Marci use for finishing her work?

What do you think Mark will do the next time so that he finishes his work on time?

How could these role plays be different?

Expanding Learning

Use pages 50 and 51 in the Activities Book to help your students

- remember the skills to completing their work
- think about important points involved in checking their work

Use pages 118 through 125 in the Picture Book to help your students improve skills for finishing their work by

- getting started
- avoiding distractions
- working at the appropriate rate
- rewarding themselves for completing their schoolwork

Use page 52 in the Activities Book to help your students review the skills they have learned for finishing their work. Have your students suggest when and how they could practice these skills. For example, they may say

"I will finish my science page on time."

"I will check my science."

"I will put my science page on the teacher's tray."

"I will say to myself, 'I'm so glad I finished.' "

Visualization

Have your students get in comfortable positions to relax. Then say, "Imagine that you feel good because you have finished your schoolwork.

"Your teacher gave the directions and told you to have your work finished by 10:15. You listened carefully. Then, you got all the materials you needed, and you started right to work. When you heard two students talking across the room, you tried hard to keep working.

"You looked at the clock to see how much time was left. At 10:10, you finished the last part. You laid your pencil down and checked your paper. You read each part and asked yourself, 'Have I left out any answers? Is each answer correct? Is my name on my paper? Is my work neat?'

"When you could answer yes to each question, you put your paper on your teacher's desk, just as she had said. You told yourself, 'I did a good job!' It was 10:15. It felt good to finish your work on time."

Handling Your Feelings

In this unit, your students will learn that it's always the right time to be their own good friends. The lesson activities will help your students accept and handle their feelings by learning to think of their feelings as good friends who help them.

The two previous units have focused on helping your students learn skills to build friendships and fit in with school expectations. This unit will help your students develop a measure of self-awareness in order to handle their own feelings.

Your students need adequate language and vocabulary to describe their feelings. They must be able to identify their feelings if they are to handle them.

The lessons in Unit 3 will help your students handle their feelings through practice with the following social language skills:

Lesson 1: Recognizing their own feelings.

Lesson 2: Using feeling words to describe their feelings.

Lesson 3: Recognizing their own angry feelings and choosing wise responses.

Lesson 4: Recognizing and managing fearful feelings.

Lesson 5: Rewarding their own strengths and achievements with positive self-talk and tangible rewards.

Lesson 1: Knowing How You Feel

Skills

A. Pay attention to your body feelings.

B. Give your feeling a name.

C. Tell yourself, "I feel . . . ."

Materials

Activities Book:
pages 54 though 56

Picture Book:
pages 126 through 133

Introduction

Many students don't know how to listen to their feelings for many reasons. They might find feelings confusing because they can feel many different ways at the same time. Or they may have learned to cover up their feelings. Some students might be afraid to admit negative feelings because they think these feelings are wrong. Strong, positive feelings may also be scary because your students might not be comfortable expressing love and concern. Your students must learn to be aware of their feelings before they can manage their feelings successfully.

Teaching your students to pay attention to their feelings will help them create positive images of themselves. Students who accept their feelings will move toward a healthy sense of power that can give them good self-esteem. When your students respect their feelings, they'll begin to see themselves as capable, responsible individuals in school, at home, and in the community.

Goals

In this lesson, your students will learn to recognize and respect their feelings. The activities will help your students

- think of their feelings as friends who help them
- pay closer attention to their feelings

Preparation

Create an atmosphere in your room that will help your students feel cared for and accepted. When your students feel valued, they'll have the freedom to develop self-awareness.

Sometimes, acknowledging a feeling can be the first step to changing it. Help your students understand that holding feelings down, pushing them back, or keeping them inside only makes feelings stay. Your students may pretend not to feel, but they feel anyway. Ignoring feelings isn't the answer.

Teaching your students to attach names to their feelings can help them become more aware of their emotions. Through your encouragement, your students will begin to accept their emotions as friends.

Social Skills Story

Use page 126 in the Picture Book with this story. Ask, "How many of these emotions have you felt today: Happy? Sad? Proud? Excited? Angry? Confused? Sometimes it's hard to know why we feel a certain way. We just feel happy, or we might be in a bad mood. It's important to think about the emotions we're feeling. We'll understand ourselves better and others will understand us better, too. Our feelings can be our friends. That's what Chee thinks. Listen to this story."

Chee came home from school one afternoon and walked quietly into the kitchen. "How was your day at school, Chee?" Chee's grandmother asked.

Chee sadly said, "Oh, it was all right, Grandmother."

Chee's grandmother said, "That's not a very enthusiastic reaction, Chee. Is something bothering you?"

Chee answered, "Well, Grandmother, there's a party that a lot of kids at school are going to. But I wasn't invited."

"How does that make you feel?" asked Chee's grandmother.

"I feel horrible," Chee said. "My friend doesn't like me."

Chee's grandfather joined the discussion, "It's all right to feel horrible about being left out. You know, everyone feels a little left out sometimes, and finds it hard to talk about. Last week, I felt awful when my friend, Mr. Lee, didn't show up when we were supposed to have lunch together."

"And I don't feel good, either, when some of our customers decide to go to another store," said Grandmother. "Let's see if we can think of a name for the way we feel when we're left out."

Chee thought for a minute, "Well, I feel sad when I think about the other kids having fun at the party without me. My friend doesn't want me. It makes me sad."

Chee's grandfather said, "That's the way to listen to your feelings, Chee. Now, let's see what we can do to help you feel less sad. Tell us about some times when you don't feel left out."

Chee said, "I don't feel left out when Bonnie calls me on the phone, or when I play kick ball on the school team."

"That's right," said Grandmother.

Chee said, "Thanks! I feel better now that we've talked about this."

Questions for Discussion

Say, "Let's talk about the story and think of some skills for understanding how we feel." Write the skills on the chalkboard or a flip chart as your students respond.

1. What do you think about this sentence? "My feelings are my good friends."

   Answers will vary.

2. How can we make good friends with our feelings?

   pay attention to how our body feels (Write **Pay attention to your body feelings.***)*

3. When Chee said she felt horrible, she hadn't decided on a name for her feelings, but she knew they weren't pleasant feelings. Name some unpleasant feelings.

   angry, sad, afraid, jealous, hurt, lonely, guilty

4. Name some pleasant feelings.

   happy, excited, hopeful, loved, proud

5. What did Chee do to begin to understand what her horrible feelings were telling her?

   She thought about what she could call her horrible feelings. (Write **Give your feeling a name.***)*

6. Why do you think it was hard for Chee to know how she felt?

   Answers will vary.

7. We can understand ourselves better when we know how we feel. What can you say to yourself after you have named your feeling?

   Answers will vary. (Write **Tell yourself, "I feel . . . ."***)*

8. True or false? Chee couldn't make her friend invite her to the party, but she could decide how she would feel about not being invited.

   true

Social Skills Activities

Skill A
Pay Attention to Your Body Feelings

1. Make a banner that says: My Feelings are My Good Friends. Remind your students that it's important for them to listen to their feelings. Encourage your students to imagine that their feelings are good friends who talk to them. Then, have your students write or talk about how feelings are like good friends.

2. Provide a large mirror so your students can study their expressions and body stance. Discuss how their bodies express what they feel. Suggest that when someone feels happy, he may walk with a bounce in his steps. When someone is sad, she might slump or shuffle her feet.

3. Sing various verses of "If You're Happy and You Know It, Clap Your Hands." Ask your students to suggest different movements and different emotions. For example, "If you're proud and you know it, stand up tall."

4. Discuss ways your students' bodies react to various feelings. Sweaty palms, faster heartbeat, dry mouth, hot cheeks, blushing, tense muscles, or a queasy stomach are examples of how student's bodies can react to certain feelings. With your older students, you might discuss several idioms related to feelings, such as

   butterflies in my stomach
   shaking in his boots
   pull yourself together
   my heart's in my throat

5. Ask your students to complete the following sentence orally or on paper. "I feel _____ when _____." Encourage your students to illustrate their sentences. Then, ask volunteers to share their descriptions.

Skill B

Give Your Feeling a Name

1. Brainstorm a list of feelings with your students and write them on a large poster. Then, have volunteers draw faces beside each feeling to show the appropriate expression. Hang the poster in a prominent place so it can help your students name and identify their feelings.

2. Let your students experience feelings in a nonthreatening atmosphere. Write the following phrases on the chalkboard:

   proud as a peacock
   brave as a lion
   sick as a dog
   dog tired
   happy as a clam
   mad as a hornet
   sly as a fox
   quiet as a mouse

   Then, have your students work in pairs to act out the phrases for other students to guess both the animal and the emotion. Encourage your students to make up their own phrases.

3. Give your students opportunities to tell or write about personal experiences. Use sentence starters like

   I feel happy when . . .

   When someone says something nice about me, I . . .

   When I make a mistake, I . . .

   I'm proud of myself for . . .

   I feel upset when . . .

   When I feel angry, I . . .

   I'm worried about . . .

Skill C

Tell Yourself, "I Feel . . . ."

1. Knowing a feeling's name will help your students know how to do something about it. If possible, take pictures of your students doing various activities at school. Let them label the pictures with the sentence, "I feel . . . ."

   Or, ask your students to bring pictures of themselves from home to label and put on a bulletin board.

2. Ask your students to complete the sentence, "I feel . . .," as you read aloud the following sentences with the appropriate intonation:

   I'm not invited to a classmate's party, but my best friend is. I feel . . . . *sad, rejected, jealous, angry*

   I dream of being an Olympic gymnast someday. I feel . . . . *hopeful, excited*

   My friend laughs at my picture. I feel . . . . *embarrassed, sad, angry*

   My friend crashes my kite. I feel . . . . *mad, angry, disappointed, sad*

I'm sleeping over at my best friend's house tonight. I feel . . . . *excited, happy*

I ran into my baby brother and he fell. I feel . . . . *sad, guilty, sorry*

I hear applause after I read a poem aloud. I feel . . . . *happy, proud, excited*

I can't tie a bow even when I try hard. I feel . . . . *frustrated, sad, mad*

My stepmom tells me she loves me. I feel . . . . *happy, loved*

Additional Activities

Role-Playing

Review the story in this lesson. Then, select one or both of the following role-play activities.

Choose volunteers to play Chee and Bonnie. Pretend that Chee is looking at an invitation in Bonnie's hand. The invitation is for a party that Chee's not invited to, but Bonnie is. Remind the student playing Chee to use the skills for knowing how she feels. Encourage the student playing Bonnie to tell Chee about the times she likes to be with her.

Choose volunteers to play Sarah and her new friend, Jordan. Pretend that today at school Jordan asked Sarah to be sure to sit beside him on the bus after school. Remind the student playing Sarah to use the skills for knowing how she feels.

Role-Play Feedback

Encourage the rest of your students to give helpful feedback to the role-play volunteers. Use the following questions:

What did you like about each character's part?

What skills did Chee use for knowing how she feels?

How could you tell Sarah was paying attention to her feelings?

How could these role plays be different?

Expanding Learning

Use pages 54 and 55 in the Activities Book to help your students

- accept their feelings as good friends who help them take care of themselves
- understand that it's okay to show their feelings

Use pages 126 through 133 in the Picture Book to help your students

- identify their feelings
- name various feelings
- understand that everyone has feelings
- remember that their emotions help them care for themselves

Use page 56 in the Activities Book to help your students review the skills learned for knowing how they feel. Have your students suggest when and how they can practice these skills. For example, a student may say

"My body feels sick when I take a test."

"My feeling's name is nervous."

"I feel nervous."

Visualization

Have your students get in comfortable positions to relax. Then say, "Close your eyes and imagine that you know how to describe your feelings.

"You have an aunt who has known for a long time that you've wanted a puppy. On your birthday, she walks in your front door. Your aunt is carrying a soft, cuddly puppy. It's the cutest puppy you've ever seen. You jump up and down. You smile and laugh out loud when the puppy licks your face. It's easy to decide what to call this pleasant feeling. You feel happy! You say to yourself, 'I feel very happy.' You're glad you know how to listen to your feelings."

Lesson 2: Saying How You Feel

Skills

A. What are you feeling?

B. Ask, "What's the smart choice?"

Say, "I feel . . . ."

Talk to someone.

Do something fun.

C. Do it! Try your best choice.

Materials

Activities Book:
pages 57 through 59

Picture Book:
pages 134 through 141

Introduction

Many students have difficulty expressing their feelings. Often, these students have poor self-esteem. Educators find that self-esteem is nurtured at school when students learn to

- feel comfortable expressing their feelings
- say what they think or feel without upsetting others
- take responsibility for their own feelings

When students assert themselves positively, they usually have good self-esteem. Self-assertion is a skill that enables your students to stick up for their own rights. Understanding their own rights, however, goes hand in hand with respecting the rights of others. Students who respect the rights of others tend to express their own feelings properly. These students usually have many friends and high self-esteem.

Goals

In this lesson, your students will practice expressing their feelings in responsible ways. The activities will help your students learn

- that everyone experiences feelings
- it's best to acknowledge their feelings
- ways to deal with their feelings responsibly

Preparation

Create an empathetic atmosphere in your classroom so students feel free to express their feelings. Express your care and concern for your students. Students who experience empathy from those they admire learn that their feelings are important.

Teach your students that a responsible way to express their feelings is to begin the statement with "I." This procedure is recommended by Thomas Gordon who calls such statements "I-messages."[1] Try expressing your own feelings with your students by starting sentences with I. For example say, "I am very frustrated because I spent several hours planning this activity, and nobody's listening." This kind of message doesn't seem to blame the class, like saying, "You students aren't good listeners!" does.

Tell your students that they can decide how to respond once they know how they feel. Then, guide your students to be

[1] Gordon, T. *T.E.T.: Teacher Effectiveness Training.* New York: David McKay Company, Inc., 1974.

responsible for their feelings by using I-messages instead of you-messages when they express their feelings. Saying "I feel mad," for example, is taking responsibility for your own feelings. But saying "You made me mad," is blaming someone else.

Social Skills Story

Use page 134 in the Picture Book with this story. Say, "Have you ever felt disappointed, sad, and worried at the same time? What could cause you to feel that way? It was hard for Bonnie to handle these feelings. Listen to this story."

One Saturday afternoon, Bonnie was playing with Nikia. Playing with Nikia wasn't what Bonnie had planned to do that afternoon. She had planned to play with Marci.

Bonnie heard the clock on the wall chime four times. Two hours had passed since Marci had promised to come to play. Bonnie sighed.

Bonnie's Aunt Dean noticed Bonnie's sigh. She said, "I can understand how disappointed you must feel, Bonnie." She knew Bonnie had been excited about Marci's visit.

Bonnie's shoulders drooped and her voice sounded sad. "Yeah," she said slowly. "I guess she's just not coming."

Then, Bonnie walked to the window and stood beside her aunt. Bonnie said sadly, "Now I don't have anyone to play in the water sprinkler with. It's not fun without Marci." Then, Bonnie became worried and said, "Maybe she doesn't like me anymore. Oh no, what if she doesn't like me? Then, I wouldn't have her as a friend."

Aunt Dean put her arm around Bonnie and said, "Sometimes talking about your feelings can help you feel better, Bonnie. You seem to feel sad and disappointed, but you're also worried. Feelings are tricky because we can feel more than one way at the same time."

Lesson 2: Saying How You Feel, *continued*

Questions for Discussion

Say, "Bonnie was able to talk to her aunt. Let's think of some other skills Bonnie could follow next time to handle her feelings." Write the skills on the chalkboard or a flip chart as your students respond.

1. Bonnie is confused about the way she feels because she feels sad, disappointed, and worried at the same time. How can she begin to sort out her feelings?

   name her feelings (Write **What are you feeling?***)*

2. What choices did Bonnie have for handling her feelings?

   Answers will vary. (Write **Ask, "What's the smart choice?"***)*

3. True or false? Saying, "I feel sad," "I feel disappointed," or "I feel worried" is one way Bonnie could have taken responsibility for the way she felt.

   true

4. Which would be a better way for Bonnie to talk about her feelings: "You make me sad" or "I feel sad"? Why?

   I feel sad. Other people don't make us feel anything; we are responsible for our own feelings. (Write **Say, "I feel . . . . "***)*

5. Bonnie is sad because Marci didn't come over when she said she would. What could Bonnie do to find out why Marci didn't come over?

   Bonnie could talk to Marci. (Write **Talk to someone.***)*

6. It helped Bonnie to talk about her feelings. But she still felt sad. What are some things that Bonnie could do to make herself feel happier?

   Answers will vary. (Write **Do something fun.***)*

7. After Bonnie thinks about her choices, what should she do?

   Do it! (Write **Do it! Try your best choice.***)*

8. One way Bonnie could talk with Marci about how she felt is to use this sentence as a guide. "When you ______ , I felt ______ because ______ ." How could Bonnie use this sentence to tell Marci about her feelings?

   When you didn't come over to play, I felt sad / disappointed because I was so excited about the fun we would have had playing in the yard with the water sprinkler.

Social Skills Activities

Skill A

What Are You Feeling?

1. Get your students to talk about what makes them feel happy, sad, embarrassed, scared, worried, or angry. Provide a large bag decorated with sad, happy, embarrassed, scared, worried, and angry faces. Next, give each student six circles. Ask your students to draw a sad face, a happy face, an embarrassed face, a scared face, a worried face, and an angry face. Have yourself or your students write the feelings on the circles under the faces. Then, collect the circles and put them in the bag. Have each student take turns choosing a circle from the bag, naming the feeling expressed by the face, and telling about a time he felt that way.

2. Help students become aware of how their feelings change. Lead them to discover that an unpleasant feeling in the morning doesn't mean the whole day will be bad. Feelings change quickly. We can control what we do about them.

Have the class create a poster that shows many different feelings. Ask students to look at the illustrated expressions and decide how they felt when they first came to school today. Then, have them decide how they feel right now. Encourage them to think of things they expect to do later in the day and anticipate how they'll feel then.

Skill B

Ask, "What's the Smart Choice?"

Say, "I Feel . . . ."

1. Suggest that talking about feelings appropriately can build friendships. Expressing positive feelings towards others is a good way to start. Give students six-inch smile faces made from construction paper. Print this short sentence in the circle, "When you ______, I feel happy."

   Tell your students that they'll write about something nice someone in the class does that makes them feel happy. When all students are done, encourage each student to read her sentence aloud and hand the smile face to the person she wrote about in her sentence, or display the faces on a bulletin board.

2. Help students use "I feel" sentences to talk about their feelings. They'll learn that this sentence helps them to understand others and themselves better. Have each student face a partner. Have your students take turns saying sentences beginning with "I think," "I feel," or "I want." For example, a student may tell another student, "I feel happy when I get a 100% on a spelling test."

   After five minutes, ask your students if they learned anything new about their partners. Then, ask them if they discovered anything about themselves.

3. Use different methods for encouraging "I feel" statements. For example, praise students for being open about feelings. If a student says, "I hate it when Briana calls me stupid," say, "I understand that you feel angry." Encourage older students to write several feelings a day in a notebook. Begin each one with "I ______." "I'm glad my parents are polite to my friends," not "My parents are nice." In this way they express their own feelings, not someone else's.

4. Help younger students list feelings, like *sleepy, happy,* and *scared.* Then, have them put the list in a hierarchy from most comfortable to least comfortable. Encourage your students to practice telling their feelings to a stuffed animal, a doll, a puppet, or an imaginary friend.

Talk to Someone

1. Sometimes, talking to someone about how you feel makes you feel better. Listen to the sentences below and tell who you would like to talk to:

   You're disappointed because you thought you'd get a puppy for your birthday.

   You're happy because you were chosen to be the lead in the school play.

   You're disappointed because you didn't go out for dinner.

   You're disappointed because your friend said he couldn't play with you on Saturday.

   You're sad because all your friends got to stay up late to play and you had to go to bed.

   You're sad because you couldn't sleep over at your friend's house because you were sick.

Do Something Fun

1. Sometimes, you need to cheer up. Have your students brainstorm activities that they could do to cheer themselves up. They may suggest activities like drawing a picture, listening to music, and calling a friend. Make a list of their suggestions. Give each student a copy of the list to refer to if she needs ideas for cheering herself up.

Skill C

Do It! Try Your Best Choice

1. Ask volunteers to role-play scenes where someone makes them sad. Then, have them choose how they'll deal with their feelings.

Additional Activities

Role-Playing

Review the story in this lesson. Then, select one or more of the following role-play activities.

Choose volunteers to play Bonnie and Marci. Pretend that Bonnie calls Marci and tells her how she feels about her not coming over to play when she promised to. Pretend that Marci couldn't come over because Marci's aunt made a surprise visit. Remind the person playing Bonnie to say, "I feel. . . ."

Choose volunteers to play Jonathan and José. Pretend that Jonathan and José go outside for recess. José is thinking about his sick dog. Jonathan asks José why he's so quiet. Remind the student playing José to use the skills learned for saying how you feel.

Choose volunteers to play Mark and Chee. Pretend that Chee was playing with a ball on the playground. Mark wanted to play, too, but Chee wouldn't share. Remind the person playing Mark to use the skills learned for saying how you feel.

Role-Play Feedback

Encourage the rest of your students to give helpful feedback to the role-play volunteers. Use the following questions:

What did you like about each character's part?

How did Bonnie express how she felt?

How did José express how he felt?

How did Mark express how he felt?

How could these role plays be different?

Expanding Learning

Use pages 57 and 58 in the Activities Book to help your students

- learn more about talking about their feelings in ways that won't upset others
- take responsibility for their own feelings

Use pages 134 through 141 in the Picture Book to help your students improve skills in saying how they feel by

- feeling comfortable expressing feelings
- considering choices they have in responding to their feelings
- using "I-messages" appropriately

Use page 59 in the Activities Book to help your students review the skills they have learned for saying how they feel. Have your students suggest when and how they can practice these skills. For example, they may say

"I'm feeling sad."

"My smart choice is to talk to someone."

"I'm going to talk to someone."

Visualization

Have your students get in comfortable positions to relax. Then, say "Close your eyes and remember a time when you talked about your feelings.

"In the lunchroom, you pick up your tray and head for your table. Suddenly, you step on something wet and you fall. Your tray crashes to the floor. Food splashes everywhere. The spoon and fork clatter as they hit the hard tile floor. You're not hurt, but your cheeks feel hot because you think other students are laughing at you. Your teacher comes to help you up. She asks if you're okay. You're glad to see her. You smile a little and say, 'I'm okay.'

"Then you think about how you feel. 'I'm pretty embarrassed that I fell in front of everybody and dropped my lunch tray,' you tell your teacher. She smiles and says, 'That's normal. Everyone feels a little embarrassed falling in front of others. I'm glad you're not hurt. Come on, let's get you another tray.' You're glad you understand your feelings enough to say how you feel. You know that feeling words are your good friends."

Lesson 3: When You're Angry

Skills

A. Stop and calm down.

B. Think of some choices.

Tell the person why you're angry.

Leave for a while.

Relax.

Talk to an adult.

C. Try your best choice.

Materials

Activities Book:
pages 60 through 62

Picture Book:
pages 142 through 149

Introduction

Many students handle anger in unhealthy ways. At times, they may react impulsively to anger. These students have difficulty feeling angry without responding in unpleasant, anti-social ways. So they fight, throw tantrums, or lash out verbally. In other instances, they may deny anger. When your students deny anger, they're not dealing with it honestly. These reactions to anger can lower self-esteem and cause other problems.

Other students have probably learned to let anger work for them. These students are able, for example, to speak up when they're angry so people will listen to them and change the things that are bothering them. These students know that their angry thoughts and feelings come when they want something they can't have. Their feelings can serve as a signal to resolve their frustration. Your students can achieve their wishes or choose an alternative desire if they deal with their angry feelings properly.

Goals

In this lesson, your students will learn to release their anger in ways that will build confidence in their abilities. Your students will learn to interact with others when problems arise in their relationships. The activities will help your students

- stop and recognize their angry feelings instead of denying they're angry
- realize they have choices in ways to respond when they're angry
- let their anger work for them

Preparation

Discuss words that are synonyms for anger. Tell your students that anger is a strong, unfavorable feeling. You can feel angry at an unfortunate event, at yourself, or at another person. *Rage*, a feeling stronger than anger, is when you lose control of yourself. *Fury* is even stronger. Someone who is furious may pound his fist on the wall, throw something down, or stomp his feet.

Have volunteers demonstrate how their bodies show anger. Have other students describe the body language they see, like a wrinkled forehead, a frown, hands on hips, and stomping feet. Model ways to handle anger so people around you don't become upset. Review the use of "I-messages" in Unit 3, Lesson 2 as a means of handling anger. Model ways to express anger. Remind your students it's okay if they're angry. Your students need to know that some reactions to anger aren't okay.

If you feel anger when your students have made careless mistakes on an assignment, say "I'm feeling angry because you're making needless mistakes on this paper." Avoid blaming your class. By expressing your feelings of frustration in an I-message, you're telling your students what is creating the problem and how you feel. You'll be modeling a way for them to deal with their own anger.

Social Skills Story

Use page 142 in the Picture Book with this story. Introduce the idea that it's wise to deal with anger when it first occurs. Say, "Knowing what to do when you feel angry can be a problem. Is learning how to act when you feel angry something you need to work on? Jonathan did. Listen to this story."

Jonathan put his lunch box on a table in the lunchroom and sat at his usual place between Mark and Marci. The children opened their lunch boxes and put their sandwiches and fruit in front of them. Jonathan's mouth watered as he opened his thermos. "I'm having apple juice today, not milk," he told Marci. "I'm so thirsty."

Before Jonathan could take a sip, however, he heard Mark howling with laughter. Mark, who was talking to Bonnie, quickly turned toward Jonathan to share why he was laughing. For the second day in a row, Mark had accidently knocked over Jonathan's thermos.

Jonathan grabbed for the thermos, but it was too late. He watched the juice soak into his sandwich. What a mess! Jonathan wasn't happy about Mark's accident. Jonathan could feel his face getting hot with anger.

Jonathan was so mad at Mark. He shouted, "Mark, you're a rotten friend. Next time, I'll spill your milk all over your food and you can eat a wet sandwich!"

Mark shouted back, "Jonathan, it was an accident. What's the big, hairy deal?"

Questions for Discussion

Say, "Let's think of skills Jonathan can use the next time he's angry." Write the skills on the chalkboard or a flip chart as your students respond.

1. What should Jonathan have done when he first felt himself getting angry: a) yell at Mark, the person who made him angry, or b) do something to make himself stop and calm down?

   calm down (Write **Stop and calm down.***)*

2. Name two or three things Jonathan could have done to calm down.

   left for a while, counted, taken deep breaths, talked with Mark about his anger (Write **Think of some choices. Tell the person why you're angry. Leave for a while. Relax. Talk to an adult.***)*

3. After Jonathan has thought about his choices, what should he do?

   Try his best choice. (Write **Try your best choice.***)*

4. If Jonathan decided to talk to Mark, which way of talking would be better: polite words or bad language? Why?

   Polite words. Bad language could just make things worse.

Social Skills Activities

Skill A

Stop and Calm Down

1. Have students role-play things that make them mad. Use the list of examples below. Have one student narrate a situation that would make the other student angry. Have the student who's role-playing anger stop and calm down by counting and taking a deep breath. The student can then choose what he'll do next to handle his anger.

   Someone stepped on your shoelace and you fell.

   Someone said, "That's an ugly shirt. Did you get it at the dump?"

   Someone spilled glue all over the picture you were going to give to your teacher.

   A friend of yours walked home with someone else and left you behind.

   A classmate asked all the other students in class to a party, but said you couldn't come because she didn't like you.

   You found out your little brother scratched your bike.

Skill B

Think of Some Choices

Tell the Person Why You're Angry

1. Let students practice expressing anger by using polite words and a firm tone of voice. Explain that their goal is to get people to listen to them and to change what is bothering them. Have your students begin their statements with the word "I" instead of "you." Let them practice completing this sentence: "I feel angry when ______ because ______."

Leave for a While

1. Discuss when you should walk away from an argument. Sometimes the best response to conflict is to walk away or even give in. In many cases, however, walking away only puts off the time when you must deal with the situation.

   Remind students that when they choose this solution, they should ask the teacher for permission to leave the classroom for a few minutes. Have students brainstorm when they think would be good times to walk away from situations.

Relax

1. Sometimes the best response is to calm your body's reaction to angry thoughts by consciously relaxing. You'll find a relaxation technique outlined in the Appendix . Use it to teach your students to counteract their feelings of anger. After your students relax, they can simply repeat the word *relax* to help them release tension.

   For a quick relaxation technique, try the following one. Smile to yourself and clench your teeth. Take a deep breath and hold it. Breathe out slowly, let your mouth drop open, and think about relaxing. Consciously feel the tension draining out of your body from your head to your toes.

Talk to an Adult

1. Say to your students, "For serious situations where you might get hurt, talk to an adult. An adult can help you or tell you about services that can help you." Have students brainstorm times when they should tell somebody if they're angry about something serious.

Skill C

Try Your Best Choice

1. Have students role-play the following situations and choose skills that will help them deal with their feelings of anger:

   Someone kicked the ball to you and it hit your face.

   You tripped on a stone and fell down the steps.

   You spilled chocolate milk all over the shirt you were going to wear to school.

   You went to sit down and a friend took away your chair and you fell.

   Someone got the last sticker that you wanted.

Additional Activities

Role-Playing

Review the story in this lesson. Then, select one or both of the following role-play activities.

Choose volunteers to play Jonathan and Mark. Pretend that Jonathan didn't yell when Mark knocked over his juice. Remind the student playing Jonathan to stop and calm down and think of some choices for what to do when he's angry.

Choose volunteers to play Steve and Kiendra. On Fridays in gym class, students can choose their own activities. Steve wants to use the only jump rope that has moveable handles. Kiendra beat Steve to the jump rope for the third Friday this month. Kiendra won't share the jump rope with Steve. Remind the person playing Steve to use the skills learned for handling anger.

Role-Play Feedback

Encourage the rest of your students to give helpful feedback to the role-play volunteers. Use the following questions:

What did you like about each character's part?

What did Jonathan do to handle his anger?

What did Steve do to handle his anger?

How could these role plays be different?

Expanding Learning

Use pages 60 and 61 in the Activities Book to help your students

- distinguish angry feelings
- choose ways to deal with those feelings

Use pages 142 through 149 in the Picture Book to help your students understand that their angry feelings can be good. They can be signals to remind students to choose effective ways to handle frustrating problems.

Use page 62 in the Activities Book to help your students review the skills they have learned for what to do when they're angry. Have your students suggest when and how they'll practice these skills. For example, they might say

"I will stop and think."

"I can tell Jerry why I'm angry."

"I will tell him that I'm angry because now I don't have a green crayon to finish my drawing."

Visualization

Have your students get in comfortable positions to relax. Then say, "Close your eyes and imagine you're angry.

"Your teacher has handed you a spelling paper with a very low grade on it. You feel angry with your teacher. Your angry feelings make your face change so you look angry. Your muscles tighten and you feel your fists clench. You're so angry that you imagine your teacher slipping on a banana peel.

"Next, you stop your angry thoughts and calmly begin counting to ten. Then, you think of your choices and name them to yourself. You can leave the room, try to relax, or tell your teacher how you feel. You decide to tell your teacher your feelings.

"You go to your teacher and say, 'I felt very angry when I saw the low grade you gave me.' Your teacher listens to you and thinks for a moment. Then she says, 'I can understand your feelings. But I wonder . . . did you study enough last night?'

"You remember that you watched TV instead of studying. And you say, 'Oh, I guess I should have studied more.' Your teacher says, 'I'm glad you told me your feelings. You'll do better on your next paper.' When you go back to your desk, you feel glad that you handled your anger so well."

Lesson 4: When You're Afraid

Skills

A. Are you afraid?

B. What are you afraid of?

C. What's the smart choice?

Do it anyway.

Leave.

Talk with someone about it.

D. Try your best choice.

Materials

Activities Book:
pages 63 through 65

Picture Book:
pages 150 through 157

Introduction

Students who manage fear well listen to their fearful feelings in dangerous situations and seek safety. These students don't allow everyday fears to keep them from taking part in new activities.

Some students go through life without fearing anything. Other students face everyday challenges cautiously. Still others see life as a never-ending series of frightening experiences. The ways students respond to fears either build or destroy their self-esteem. Students who run away from every new experience miss out on enriching activities that could lead to social and emotional growth. But students who take unnecessary risks in the face of real danger can get hurt.

Your students need to develop skill and confidence in their own abilities to handle their fears. Improving their ability to deal with fear can increase their self-confidence. That's why teaching your students wise ways to handle their fears is important.

Goals

In this lesson, your students will learn to deal with their everyday fears. The activities will help your students

- distinguish between real fear and things they fear might happen
- face everyday fears instead of giving in to them

Preparation

Help your students understand that being afraid is not something to be ashamed of. While different things make people afraid, everyone feels afraid sometimes. We usually can't control our fearful thoughts and feelings, so we shouldn't think less of anyone for showing fear. It's what we do with fear and how we handle it that's important.

Let students take turns answering the question, "What is something that makes you a little afraid?" You may share something you're afraid of. Stress the fact that fear is a normal emotion. When students understand that fear is normal, they might discuss their fears more openly.

Tell your students that they might feel fear about something that could really happen. Your students might also feel fear about things that couldn't really happen. Ask your students to name some events that could happen to create fear, like a stranger following them. Then, discuss things that couldn't happen, but still might create fear, like having monsters under their beds. Help your students understand that some new experiences might seem scary, but they aren't truly dangerous. Experiences such as performing on a stage or staying overnight with a friend the first time aren't truly dangerous.

Social Skills Story

Use page 150 in the Picture Book with this story. Say, "Have you ever been afraid someone would laugh at you if you did something on a stage? José almost missed out on some fun because of his fear. Listen to this story."

José stepped off the bus and ran toward the door to the YMCA like he did every afternoon. José belonged to an after-school Boys' Club where he learned tumbling. José liked tumbling because he had learned to do cartwheels and somersaults. He worked hard at getting his body movements just right. In fact, he had become an excellent tumbler.

When José walked through the door, he was surprised to see his coach, Mr. Mendez, waiting for him. "Hi José. I'd like you to be the lead tumbler in our act for the City Dance Revue next month," Mr. Mendez said.

José didn't know what to do. He knew the City Dance Revue was an important show where hundreds of people came to see children from all over the city dance and do gymnastics.

José was frightened about getting on the stage with everyone watching him. He was scared he might forget part of the act. He imagined everyone would laugh at him. José began to breathe faster and got sweaty palms when he thought about their laughter. These fears made him want to tell the coach that he didn't want to be in the show.

Then, after a while, he had other thoughts. He imagined how great it would be if he did a good job and everyone applauded. José had mixed feelings about being in the City Dance Revue.

Questions for Discussion

Say, "Let's talk about the story and make a list of skills for handling fear." Write the skills on the chalkboard or a flip chart as your students respond.

1. José knows he needs to listen to his body because his body tells him about his feelings. How was José's body acting when he thought about his fears?

   faster breathing and sweaty palms

2. Feelings can be tricky. Sometimes it's hard to name the feeling your body is telling you about. So you need to ask yourself what you're feeling. What feeling did José have?

   fear (Write **Are you afraid?***)*

3. It's important to know exactly what thing you're afraid of. What was José's biggest fear?

   people's laughter if he made a mistake (Write **What are you afraid of?***)*

4. When you're afraid, you need to do something about it. Why?

   so you won't be afraid anymore (Write **What's the smart choice?***)*

5. Were people laughing at José, or did José think people were going to laugh at him?

   He thought people were going to laugh at him.

6. What are some choices José could make to handle his fear?

   tell the coach he wouldn't take the part, take the part and do his best, talk with someone about his fear (Write **Do it anyway. Leave. Talk with someone about it.***)*

7. José still wasn't sure, but he decided what the best choice would be. What should he do next?

   try it (Write **Try your best choice.***)*

Social Skills Activities

Skill A

Are You Afraid?

1. Whether you're afraid of something that's happening or of something you think will happen, your body responds in the same way. You might notice a fast heartbeat, rapid breathing, dry mouth, sweaty palms, and goose bumps. Tell your students to listen to their bodies when they feel afraid. Their bodies prepare them to face the feared situation or run away from a dangerous situation.

Skill B

What Are You Afraid Of?

1. You can make students aware that fears are common to everyone. Confessing to a fear isn't bad. Show your students this by asking the question in the Preparation section of this lesson. Once feared objects or things have been identified, ask why someone might fear them. Help students understand there's always a reason for fear. Students might not make the connection between their feelings and the specific basis for the fear. Thinking of fear in relation to something really happening can help students begin to control their fearful feelings.

Skill C

What's the Smart Choice?

Do It Anyway

1. In order to make a choice in how to handle your fear, you have to understand your fear. Is the fear a warning of real danger? Or is the fear an everyday fear? Perhaps, it's a fear of something you don't understand.

   When students are scared, let them know you understand. Encourage them to talk about their fears. Then, talk about ways your students can overcome their fears. Explain to your students that they need to overcome their fears, but only when they're ready.

   Let your students think of everyday fears that when faced, help them become more confident. They may mention going away to camp for the first time, joining a new club, going to the first day of school, staying overnight at a friend's house, or being in a school play.

Leave

1. If there's a real danger, the smartest thing to do is get away as quickly as possible. Being afraid of someone who has a knife or gun, for example, is a signal to get to a safe place as quickly as possible. Have your students think of other real dangers such as storms or fires.

Talk with Someone About It

1. Sometimes the best response to fear is to talk with someone you trust. Have students list people who they could trust with their fears. Talking with someone about the fear will help students make wise choices.

Skill D

Try Your Best Choice

1. In order to handle their fears, your students need to do something about them. If the first choice doesn't work, your students might need to try another choice. Have your students tell what they would do in the following fearful situations:

   a strange man is walking behind you

   you're afraid your parents are going to get divorced

   you're afraid a spider might crawl on you in your sleep

   as you get to the door of your friend's apartment, you hear fighting

   you're afraid you might spill water as you carry a full glass from the sink to the table

   you're afraid your teacher will yell at you if you don't finish your work

---

Additional Activities

Role-Playing

Review the story in this lesson. Then, select one or both of the following role-play activities.

Choose volunteers to play José and his tumbling coach. Pretend José tells his coach his fears about being alone on the stage and having someone laugh at him. Pretend the coach is understanding.

Choose volunteers to play Kevin and his older brother Brian. Pretend that Kevin fell off his bike and skinned his knee. He's afraid of falling off his bike again. Brian thinks Kevin should ride his bike again right away. Remind the student playing Kevin to use the skills learned for handling fears.

Role-Play Feedback

Encourage the rest of your students to give helpful feedback to the role-play volunteers. Use the following questions:

What did you like about each character's part?

Did José talk through his choices?

Did Kevin need to be afraid? Why?

How did Brian feel about Kevin's fear? How could you tell?

How could these role plays be different?

Expanding Learning

Use pages 63 and 64 in the Activities Book to help your students learn to

- distinguish fear about things that are happening from fear about things they think might happen
- understand that it's okay to have fearful feelings

Use pages 150 through 157 in the Picture Book to help your students improve skills for

- protection from real danger
- increased confidence that comes when they face everyday fear and do the task at hand

Use page 65 in the Activities Book to help your students review the skills learned for handling fear. Have your students suggest when and how they can practice these skills. For example they might say

"I'm afraid."

"I'm afraid of lightning."

"The smart choice is to talk to my dad."

"I will talk to my dad."

Visualization

Have your students get in comfortable positions to relax. Say, "Close your eyes and imagine a time when you made a smart choice about handling your fear. You get off the school bus and head for your class. You realize you left your backpack on the bus, so you run back to get it. Then, you walk quickly down the hall, but you hear the school bell ring and you know you're late. At first you don't know what to do. You stand outside the door to your classroom. Your heart beats faster and faster. You're afraid your teacher will be angry with you and you won't know what to say.

"You think of your choices. Should you try to hide, go ahead and face your fear by going into your classroom, or wait until a friend comes out of the room and talk to your friend about it? You know what you must do. You take a deep breath and go into your classroom. You tell your teacher you're sorry for being late. You tell him what happened to make you late.

"Your teacher says, 'You were afraid I'd be mad at you for being late, but I was more worried that something might have happened to you. I'm glad that you came right in and told me what was wrong. Sit down and take a deep breath.' You feel relieved because you faced your fear right away, even though you were afraid your teacher would be angry. The longer it takes to face your fear, the more frightened you'll become. You're glad you chose the smart way to handle your fear."

Lesson 5: Rewarding Yourself

Skills

A. Ask, "Did I do a good job?"

B. Tell yourself, "I did a good job."

C. If you say mean things to yourself, say "Stop!"

D. Ask, "How will I reward myself?"

Materials

Activities Book:
pages 66 through 68

Picture Book:
pages 158 through 165

Introduction

Students can learn to reward themselves most effectively when they treat themselves as they would treat good friends. This way, students can accept themselves and learn from their mistakes. Your students will also see and appreciate their own strengths and the strengths of their work.

For example, let's say a student has set a goal and achieved it. He might say to himself, "I've worked hard to finish my homework correctly. Now, I'll do something nice for myself." This student sees the value of his efforts. He can feel good about himself when he knows he gave something his full effort. This student doesn't have to compare his work to the work of others.

Your students have probably already learned that teachers, parents, and peers do not always notice their good work. Therefore, students must learn to reward themselves if they're to feel good about their own efforts.

Goals

In this lesson, your students will learn when and how to reward themselves. The activities will help your students

- evaluate and reward their own good work
- replace self-critical thoughts with helpful thoughts
- list activities they can use independently or with permission to reward themselves

Preparation

Introduce the concept of self-appreciation by discussing the meanings of the words *pride*, *bragging*, and *friend*. Use the suggestions below to guide your discussion.

Pride. Tell your students that there are two kinds of pride, true pride and false pride. Ask, "What is true pride?" True pride is a feeling that comes from feeling good about yourself because of something you worked hard to achieve. Cleaning your room, helping a parent at home, being successful at a sport, or doing well on an assignment are all things that can lead to feelings of pride.

False pride may surface when people try to feel proud about something they didn't have to work to achieve, such as feeling proud of having a rich father or having naturally curly hair. There's nothing the students did to earn the father's money or the curly hair. Have your students make lists of things that could lead to feelings of true pride and false pride.

Guide your students to feel pride in their efforts by describing actions and strengths your students can feel proud of. For example, say "Darla, you must feel good about introducing yourself to the new girl on the playground today. Your friendliness helped her feel more comfortable in our class."

Bragging. Your students may confuse appreciating their own good work with bragging. Help them understand that feeling good about what they've done well is different from bragging. Explain that you are bragging when you talk too much about something you own or have done. Bragging makes others feel bad, but true pride doesn't.

Friend. Suggest that one way your students can learn to feel true pride is to talk to themselves the way a good friend would. Ask, "What is a friend?" A friend is someone who likes you, someone you can talk to. A good friend expects the best of you, but doesn't demand that you're perfect. A good friend points out your good qualities. A good friend wants to know what you've done well, but feels hurt when you brag in false pride.

Social Skills Story

Use page 158 in the Picture Book with this story. Ask your students to think of one thing they did well today. Then say, "Do you reward yourself by telling yourself you've done a good job when you know you've worked hard? Mark needs to learn to reward himself. Listen to this story."

Mark laid his paintbrush down and stood back to look at his picture. He had drawn and painted a big, blue Earth. His picture showed a clean Earth with people all over the world taking care of the planet. Mark thought, "This is a terrible picture. The colors are awful. I'll never get it in the contest."

Then, Mark saw Mrs. Sahwani walking toward his desk. She looked at his picture and said, "Mark, your picture is ready for the contest. Please put it with the other pictures."

The school art contest was called "Caring for Earth." The picture that won the school contest would enter the city contest. The picture that won the city contest would be a poster for a billboard. Mark wanted to win the contest, but he didn't think he had a chance. No one had said they liked his picture. He told himself, "My picture is ugly. I did a bad job."

After Mark handed in his picture, he worried about his work. He wasn't even excited about the contest. A couple weeks later, the students in Mark's school gathered in the auditorium to hear the announcement of the art contest winners.

To his surprise, Mark won the art contest. The principal gave him a big blue ribbon in front of all the students in the school auditorium. When Mark walked off the stage, he shook hands with the other students whose pictures were in the contest.

Questions for Discussion

Say, "Let's talk about the story and think of some skills for understanding good ways to reward ourselves." Write the skills on the chalkboard or a flip chart as your students respond.

1. True or false? It's okay to like yourself and be your own good friend. You can say nice things to yourself.

   true

2. When Mark finished his picture, how could he have decided if he had done a good job?

   ask himself if he did a good job (Write **Ask, "Did I do a good job?"***)*

3. Mark wanted someone else to tell him that his picture was good. What could he have told himself?

   that he did a good job (Write **Tell yourself, "I did a good job."***)*

4. What would have happened if Mark had told himself, "I spent a lot of time on this picture. My picture is very pretty"?

   Answers will vary.

5. Mark told himself mean things about his picture. Do you think Mark would have told his friends mean things about their pictures? Why?

   No. He wouldn't be mean to his friends.

6. How could Mark stop himself from saying such mean things to himself?

   say "Stop!" (Write **If you say mean things to yourself, say "Stop!"***)*

7. Sometimes we get rewards for things we finish. But there are many times when other people don't notice what good work we did. Then, we can reward ourselves. What are some ways that we can reward ourselves for our good work?

   Answers will vary. (Write **Ask, "How will I reward myself?"***)*

8. Do you think it's a good idea to reward yourself for your own good work? Why?

   Answers will vary.

Social Skills Activities

Skill A

Ask, "Did I Do a Good Job?"

1. For several days, have your students tell you something they like about themselves. If students have difficulty answering, try offering them choices. Ask, "Did you feel good about what you did in math class, how you played your part in the puppet show, or the way you handled your fear? What did you like about the way you shared with the new student or completed your homework?" With some students, be even more specific. Say, "You put away the paints in the art center. Did you feel good about that?"

2. Teach your students to appreciate their work. Students often think that only excellence or the best is worthy of reward. By that standard, most work wouldn't be rewarded. To practice looking at their work on its own merits, have them change "I'm the best" statements into "I enjoy . . . ," "I'm good at . . . ," or "I like . . ." statements.

   "I'm the best athlete." *"I'm good at running."*

   "I'm the best looking of all my friends." *"My hair looks nice today."*

   "I'm the most popular student." *"I have good friends."*

"I'm the best in math." *"I'm good at subtracting."*

"I'm the best singer." *"I like to sing."*

3. Students who are able to write may keep a small notebook or a journal where they list or describe good work they have completed. They may also list some of their own good qualities, such as friendliness, helpfulness, and the ability to explain things to others.

4. Have students write letters to themselves describing their good qualities. Remind your students to begin some sentences with "I'm good at . . .," "I like to . . .," or "I am . . . ." Have them put stamps on the letters and mail them to themselves. What fun they'll have reading about themselves when their letters arrive!

Skill B

Tell Yourself, "I Did a Good Job."

1. Have students divide sheets of paper into four sections. In each part, students will draw or write about activities they've completed this week. Have them put gold stars beside the activities they've done well. Help them write, "I did a good job," below those pictures or sentences.

2. Point out that good work doesn't mean perfect work. For students to feel good about themselves, they must know that they can fail or make mistakes, and still be accepted. They need to be able to say, "Even if I make mistakes or my paper isn't perfect, it doesn't mean I'm a terrible person. Nobody's work is perfect!"

   If you have some perfectionists among your students, tell them about some of your own difficulties, like "Cursive handwriting is easy enough for me now, but I made a lot of funny-looking letters before I got it right. I finally learned to tell myself I was getting better, even if my handwriting wasn't perfect. Then, I could reward my own hard work."

Skill C

If You Say Mean Things to Yourself, Say "Stop!"

1. Discuss ways that critical inner language can be hurtful. This activity can be a springboard to that discussion. Have students tell whether your examples of critical inner language or more kindly inner language are harmful or helpful. Use these examples:

   "Stupid me. How could I have made a silly mistake like that?" *harmful*

   "I'm no dummy. I can figure this problem out. I just need a little time." *helpful*

   "Good. I'm doing fine so far." *helpful*

   "Oh boy, this is going to be tough. I know I'll mess up." *harmful*

   "That's as good as I can do, but it's not what they want." *harmful*

   "I was supposed to circle answers, not underline. That's okay. I'll erase these lines carefully. There. It's okay." *helpful*

Skill D

Ask, "How Will I Reward Myself?"

1. Teach your students that there are ways they can choose to reward themselves after working hard. While students dictate, record on the chalkboard ways they think of to reward themselves without using money.

Here are some to get you started:

ask to take a break
clap your hands
hug yourself
dance
exercise
walk a dog
play with a kitten
play an instrument
whistle
blow bubbles
chew a stick of gum
ask to invite a friend over

2. Remind your students that it's important to choose a reward they enjoy! Then, they won't have to wait for someone else to make them feel good. Your students can control those feelings themselves.

   Another way to raise your students' awareness of self-rewards is for them to make a large poster. Have them arrange on the poster clippings from magazines that stand for different rewards.

Additional Activities

Role-Playing

Review the story in this lesson. Then, select one or both of the following role-play activities.

Choose a volunteer to play Mark. Pretend that Mark rewards himself for doing a good job with his picture. Remind the student playing Mark to use the skills for rewarding himself.

Choose a volunteer to play Phillip. Pretend that Phillip cleaned his room faster than usual. He did a good job. He is his own good friend. Phillip tells himself nice things about his good work. Then, Phillip rewards himself by putting together a new puzzle on the clean floor in the middle of his room.

Role-Play Feedback

Encourage the rest of your students to give helpful feedback to the role-play volunteers. Use the following questions:

What did you like about each character's part?

What nice things did Mark tell himself?

What other ways could Mark reward himself?

What nice things did Phillip tell himself?

What other ways could Phillip reward himself?

How could these role plays be different?

Expanding Learning

Use pages 66 and 67 in the Activities Book to help your students learn more about

- improving ways to talk to themselves
- choosing rewards for their good work

Use pages 158 through 165 in the Picture Book to help your students

- determine when they did a good job
- say nice things to themselves
- think of ways to reward themselves for their own good work

Use page 68 in the Activities Book to help your students review the skills learned for rewarding themselves. Have your students suggest when and how they can practice these skills.

For example, they may say

"Did I read well?"

"I did a good job reading to the class."

"Stop. I'm a good reader."

"I will pat myself on the back."

Visualization

Have your students get in comfortable positions to relax. Then say, "Close your eyes and imagine a time when you talked nicely to yourself and rewarded yourself for good work.

"You tell yourself, 'All right, what do I have to do to get my homework done? My teacher wants me to write five spelling words on a sheet of paper. Okay, I'll put my name at the top of the page just the way my teacher wants it. Now, I'll number each word and print it carefully so that every letter is in the right place. Good. I'm doing a good job on this page.

" 'I'll check to see if every word is spelled right. No, there's a letter missing. That's okay. I can erase just fine and add it. I have one more word to write. I'm done. Now, I'll reward myself for finishing my homework. I'll ask if I may go outside and ride my bike. I'm glad I know how to reward myself.' "

Using Self-Control

Feelings of competence come from more than good grades or success in sports. Your students get a sense of how capable they are by their ability to manage their emotional responses.

Many students think their parents, teachers, or friends cause them to react the way they do. It's easy to blame someone else for the way they act. Blaming others, however, is self-defeating because it leads to a sense of incompetence.

It's not easy to stop and think about what to do in stressful situations. It's easier to fight back, demand, cry, or yell back insults. Impulsive reactions, of course, only result in social problems. Often, good decisions can be made if a student can learn to control his emotions long enough to make good decisions.

The lessons in Unit 4 will help your students achieve a sense of competency in stressful situations through practice with the following social language skills:

Lesson 1: Developing strategies for cooling off when they're too angry to respond rationally.

Lesson 2: Maintaining control when teased so they can choose a strategy for dealing with teasers.

Lesson 3: Asking permission instead of acting impulsively or using another person's belongings without asking.

Lesson 4: Admitting their own mistakes and accepting the consequences.

Lesson 5: Remaining calm when they've been blamed for something they didn't do instead of lashing out or refusing to talk or listen.

Lesson 1: When You Need to Cool Off

Skills

A. Stop! Don't say a word.

B. Look at what's happening.

C. Listen to your body.

D. Think of your choices.

- Walk away.
- Talk with someone about it.
- Do a relaxation exercise.
- Write or draw about it.
- Do something you enjoy.

Materials

Activities Book:
pages 70 through 74

Picture Book:
pages 166 through 173

Introduction

Strong emotions can make it hard for you to think. That's why it's important to learn ways to delay your responses. Impulsive actions may be passive as well as aggressive. Passively, students may blame others or bottle up their anger and explode at inappropriate times. Aggressively, students may hit others, yell or scream, or shout put-downs.

Your students might not realize they can choose their responses to strong emotions. Cooling off first frees them to make effective choices, instead of impulsive reactions. When your students are upset, it's important for them to learn to stop, look, listen, and think before they act.

Goals

This lesson will help your students learn to control themselves when they're too angry or upset to identify their feelings. The activities will teach your students

- that it's important to cool off
- to choose a rational response to strong emotions
- that hurting someone with an impulsive verbal or physical response isn't appropriate
- alternatives for getting strong feelings under control

Preparation

Your students learn much about how to handle their strong feelings by watching you handle your feelings. Discuss with your students the following cues that will tell them they're getting angry:

- face gets hot
- body shakes
- heart beats faster
- hands clench to a fist
- mouth gets dry
- breathing gets faster
- muscles tighten
- eyes narrow or squint
- stomach feels sick or tight
- teeth clench

Explain that strong feelings can make it hard to think and solve problems. These strong feelings may keep a person from paying attention to what she's doing. She may later regret actions taken when she felt strong anger, embarrassment, or fear.

Say, "Name some ways we might react to strong feelings."

hit someone
give put-downs
bottle up anger inside
feel bad about yourself
think of ways to "get back"
hold grudges
run away
blame others
yell or scream

Ask your students, "What do you think happens to bottled-up anger?" They're right if they say it explodes when you least expect it to.

Social Skills Story

Use page 166 in the Picture Book with this story. Ask, "Why is it important to listen to your own body talk? Bonnie needed to learn why. Listen to this story."

Bonnie's Aunt Dean had a terrible headache, so she asked Bonnie to watch Nikia after school. Bonnie shouted, "Why do you have to be sick? Chee invited me to go shopping with her and her grandma. I want to go shopping."

Bonnie's aunt said, "I'm sorry. I know you would have a fun time with Chee, but I need some help now."

Bonnie's stomach began to feel a little sick. She was breathing faster, but she told her aunt she would watch Nikia.

"Come on Nikia. Let's get some cookies and go outside. That will be fun."

Bonnie and Nikia carried their snacks to the front porch. They sat on the steps eating cookies and drinking milk from their favorite cups.

Suddenly, Nikia spotted her tricycle under a bush beside the porch. She pointed to the tricycle and said, "I want to ride, Bonnie." So Bonnie got up to get the tricycle for Nikia.

When Bonnie reached for the tricycle, her hair got caught in the bush. When Bonnie pulled her hair loose, her favorite barrette popped out of her hair and into the air.

Bonnie began to look for the barrette. At the same time, Nikia climbed on her tricycle and headed down the sidewalk. Then, Bonnie heard a crunch. She turned around and saw her barrette crushed under the wheel of Nikia's tricycle. Bonnie groaned. To make it worse, Nikia just laughed.

Bonnie's face grew red. Her eyes squinted. She ran toward her little sister screaming, "Nikia, how could you? You broke my barrette!" Bonnie threw Nikia's favorite cup down on the sidewalk and it broke. "I hate you, Nikia!" she yelled.

When Nikia heard Bonnie's angry words, she looked into Bonnie's face. Then, the frightened Nikia started to cry.

Questions for Discussion

Say, "Bonnie lost control when she felt strong anger toward her little sister. Bonnie scared Nikia when she yelled at her, and Bonnie broke Nikia's favorite cup. Let's talk about the story and think of some skills to help Bonnie the next time she feels so angry." Write the skills on a chalkboard or a flip chart as your students respond.

1. How many times did Bonnie feel angry in this story? Explain.

   Twice. First, she felt angry when she had to watch Nikia instead of going shopping. Then, she felt angry when Nikia broke her favorite barrette.

2. How did Bonnie's body let her know she was feeling angry?

   felt sick, breathed faster, red face, squinted eyes

3. A traffic light can help you remember how to handle strong feelings, like anger. When it's red, what does it tell you?

   stop (Write **Stop! Don't say a word.***)*

4. When would it have been best for Bonnie to stop and not say a word?

   when her body told her she was getting very angry

5. What could Bonnie have looked at to remind her not to have become so angry?

   Answers will vary. (Write **Look at what's happening.***)*

6. What could Bonnie have listened to?

   her body language telling her she was getting very angry (Write **Listen to your body.***)*

7. If you stop, look, and listen, then you'll have time to think. What could Bonnie have thought about?

   Answers will vary. (Write **Think of your choices.***)*

8. How could Bonnie have relaxed?

   take a deep breath, count to ten (Write **Do a relaxation exercise.***)*

9. Walking away is another way to keep from losing control. Could Bonnie have made that choice? Why?

   No. Bonnie was watching Nikia. (Write **Walk away.***)*

10. Sometimes talking with someone helps us control angry feelings. Would that be a choice Bonnie could make? If so, who could she talk with?

    Yes. She could talk with her parents, a good friend, or her aunt. (Write **Talk with someone about it.***)*

11. Drawing a picture about our angry feelings or writing how we feel helps us think about what we can do. Do you think Bonnie could try that? Why?

    Answers will vary. (Write **Write or draw about it.***)*

12. Bonnie made a wise choice when she felt angry at her aunt. What did Bonnie do?

    Bonnie took Nikia outside for a snack. (Write **Do something you enjoy.***)*

Social Skills Activities

Skill A

Stop! Don't Say a Word

1. Explain to your students that it's hard to keep from saying something when you feel very angry. Have your students brainstorm answers to this question. "Why is it important to cool off and think?"

2. Point out that what your students think about a situation makes a difference. Everyone, after all, doesn't feel awful about the same things. Tell your students that changing their thinking about a situation is one way to change angry behavior.

   To demonstrate, ask your students to write a number between 1 and 10 (10 being really awful) to measure how awful it would be for a barrette to get broken. Have your students hand in their numbers. Then, list numbers on the chalkboard.

   Talk about the differences in the numbers. Say, "Look at the different numbers. Not everyone feels that losing a barrette is that awful. You might not be as angry as Bonnie was." Say, "Tell about something that happened to you that you thought was awful, but that might not be so bad to someone else. What made it awful to you?"

Skill B

Look at What's Happening

1. Noticing what's happening around them can help your students gain control of their strong feelings. Point out that carefully looking to see what is going on all around can help us decide what to do. When we have more information about a situation, we're better able to act wisely.

   Show the picture on page 166 in the Picture Book that goes with the story in this lesson. Then ask, "If I took a picture of everything that was happening before Bonnie yelled at Nikia, what would the picture have shown?" Point out that Bonnie was angry about missing the shopping trip before the barrette was broken. She needed to look at how she was feeling about not going shopping instead of taking her anger out on Nikia. If Bonnie had been paying attention to how her body was feeling, she may have seen that breaking the barrette was an accident and that her sister was a very young child. Ask, "How could this picture help her to cool off?"

2. Tell your students that talking about situations that usually bother them can help them control strong feelings. Perhaps by being prepared that certain situations might bother you, you'll be ready to calm yourself down before getting too angry. Say, "Let's look around for some things that bug you." List their responses. Your students may name situations like when they're teased, when their parents say no, and when their brother or sister uses their things.

3. Use your students' ideas from above to make a "Bugs Me Caterpillar." Your students will need construction paper, pipe cleaners, crayons, scissors, and glue. Have them cut out four-inch circles and glue the edges of the circles together to form the caterpillar's body. Have your students draw a caterpillar's face on the first circle and attach pipe cleaner feelers. Help your students write (or draw) things that bug them on the other circles. Make a bulletin board display with all the caterpillars.

Skill C

Listen to Your Body

1. First, write these body cues on the chalkboard or name them:

face is red
body is shaking
eyes squint
muscles tighten
arms and legs tingle
teeth are clenched
breathing gets faster
throat tightens
hands clench to fist
heart beats faster

Then, take a magic carpet ride and talk about body cues that indicate strong feelings.

You'll need carpet squares, a tape recording of Rimsky-Korsakoff's "Scheherazade" or another song, and a tape player.

Ask your students to sit on their "magic carpets" as you play "Scheherazade." Describe the following situations while your students are "flying." Ask, "What body language do we see? If your body could say what it feels, what would it say?"

I see Dan about to jump into a fight that's none of his business. What body language do we see in Dan? What body language could Dan hear if he listened?

I see Marla standing on her head and telling Zohada, "I bet you can't do this." What body language do we see in Zohada? What body language could Zohada hear if she listened?

Sherrie's brother loaned her tape player to his friend without asking Sherrie. What body language do we see in Sherrie? What body language could Sherrie hear if she listened?

The teacher accused Jefferson of cheating, but Jefferson didn't cheat. What body language do we see in Jefferson? What body language could Jefferson hear if he listened?

Krissy's parents just told her she can't go bowling. What body language do we see in Krissy? What body language could Krissy hear if she listened?

Skill D

Think of Your Choices

1. Play a robot game to emphasize that there are many ways to behave. First ask, "What are robots?" Point out that robots don't think for themselves. Robots only do what someone programs them to do. Ask volunteers to pretend to be robots while other students observe. Have the robots do the following actions on your command:

   stand up
   turn around
   walk fast
   show what an elephant does
   lose your temper
   turn around
   sit down

   Then, ask the observers what they saw:

   Did the robots have any choice in their behavior? Why?

   Do people have choices in how they will act? Why?

   Did all the robots act the same way when they heard the command? What different behaviors did you see?

   Can you remember a time when you acted differently than what you were told? Did you have a choice in how you would act?

   If you have a choice in how to act, what behaviors are better for you, yelling at someone or walking away so you won't say something mean? Why?

2. Have your students practice relaxing. Refer to the Appendix in the Instructor's Manual and practice the relaxation techniques.

Additional Activities

Role-Playing

Review the story in this lesson. Then, select one or more of the role-play activities.

Choose volunteers to play Bonnie and Nikia. Pretend that Nikia ran over Bonnie's favorite barrette with her tricycle. Bonnie thought about her angry feelings instead of yelling at Nikia. Remind the student playing Bonnie to look at what's happening and listen to her body.

Choose volunteers to play Janet and her dad. Pretend that Janet felt very angry when her dad told her that he wouldn't let her have new jeans because they're too expensive. Remind the student playing Janet to use the skills for when she needs to cool off.

Choose volunteers to play Paul and Bernie. Pretend that Bernie says to Paul, "I bet you can't hit the ball as hard as I can." Paul can't and he's angry. Have Paul do something else he enjoys.

Choose volunteers to play Chris and his mom. Pretend that Chris really wants to go on an overnight camping trip, but his mom won't let him because he didn't finish a school project. Chris walks away.

Role-Play Feedback

Encourage the rest of your students to give helpful feedback to the students who participated in the role plays. Use these questions to stimulate positive feedback:

What did you like about each character's part?

What skills did Bonnie use for cooling off?

What skills did Janet use for cooling off?

What skills did Paul use for cooling off?

What skills did Chris use for cooling off?

How could these role plays be different?

Expanding Learning

Use pages 70 through 73 in the Activities Book to help your students

- identify strong feelings
- replace upsetting thoughts with imagery of cheerful thoughts
- identify and discuss ways to control impulsive actions
- discuss differences between strong feelings and actions

Use pages 166 through 173 in the Picture Book to help your students choose ways to cool off when they're upset.

Use page 74 in the Activities Book to help your students review the skills for cooling off. Have your students think of when and how they can practice these skills. For example, they may say

"I will stop before I hurt someone's feelings."

"I will look around me."

"I will listen to my body."

"I will take a deep breath."

Visualization

Have your students get in comfortable positions to relax. Then say, "Close your eyes and imagine yourself staying calm and in control even when you feel very upset.

"You feel so upset that your jaw feels tight, your teeth are clenched, and your body is shaking. You want to scream or hit someone, but you don't. You stop yourself and don't say a word. You look at the other person and see her fists clench. You take three deep breaths, then you walk away. You ask yourself, 'Who can I talk to about this situation?' In your mind, you see the person you would talk to.

"As soon as possible, you talk with this person. You say, 'I felt so angry, I wanted to shout and hit, but I didn't.

" 'Now I need to decide what to do.' You decide that you'll go to the person and say, 'I feel angry when you call me names.' You and the other person talk about the situation and work it out. You're glad you found a way to cool off when you felt so upset."

Lesson 2: When You're Teased

Skills

A. Stop! Don't say a word.

B. Think of your choices.

Ignore the teasing.

Agree with the teasing or laugh.

Ask, "Why did you say that?"

Say, "I want you to stop."

Materials

Activities Book:
pages 75 through 77

Picture Book:
pages 174 through 181

Introduction

Teasing can be a problem that won't stop unless your students know how to handle it. Your students must understand that a teaser wants to upset the victim. This knowledge will help your students learn to change behavior that invites teasing, such as running away, crying, arguing, or fighting back. Your students will learn to stop and choose a good response to teasing.

Sometimes, it's hard to maintain self-control when you're teased. Students need to be able to recognize and express feelings and give themselves praise in order for them to handle teasing. When teasing becomes more than words, it can turn into a dangerous situation. This is especially true if teasers join forces and isolate their victim. Your students need to know when a situation is getting out of hand and get help.

A student who is teased might feel embarrassed, angry, ashamed, and scared. It's not enough to tell that student, "Don't let it upset you." She needs to learn to feel competent and in control so her behavior convinces the teasers that the teasing doesn't bother her. If your students don't know how to handle teasing, they're left feeling helpless, incompetent, and insecure. That's why learning to handle teasing is so important.

Goals

In this lesson, your students will learn ways to deal with teasing. The activities will help your students

- meet their teasers with a quiet confidence that will ultimately decrease the frequency of teasing attacks
- handle the teasing

Preparation

Recall a time when you were teased. Be ready to share the experience with your students, if appropriate. Your students may feel ashamed when they're teased. By sharing your experience, you say to your students, "I know what it's like."

Ask your students if they know the meaning of the word *tease*. Explain that other words for tease are *kid, laugh at, rib, needle, put down, ridicule,* and *make fun of*. Ask, "What are some things kids get teased about?" Then, invite your students to tell how they handle teasing. Ask, "Why is it important to learn to handle teasing?"

Social Skills Story

Use page 174 in the Picture Book with this story. Say, "Teasing others is a kind of bad fun that leaves people feeling bad about themselves. When you're the one being teased, it's no fun. Chee didn't like being teased or seeing others teased. Listen to this story."

Chee always jumped off the last step of the school bus because her legs were too short for her to step down. One day, Chee jumped off the bus, then jumped back on because an older boy shoved a younger boy in front of her.

The older boy laughed at the younger boy. "Ha, ha," he said. "You're the worst athlete in this school."

"I am not," said the younger boy.

"Are too," said the older boy.

The younger boy kept arguing back. "Am not!" Then, he started to cry.

"Look at the little crybaby," said the older boy. "Sissy!" He looked at the other students and grinned. "Look at him cry. Ha, ha."

"You're a pig!" the younger boy yelled back. He ran into the school.

The older boys shouted, "Run, run as fast as you can, crybaby."

Chee watched the older boys laughing. "That little kid must feel terrible," she thought.

Chee walked past the jeering boys and into the school. She turned a corner and headed down the long hallway toward Room 14.

Then, to Chee's surprise, she heard laughter behind her.

"Are they laughing at me?" Chee wondered.

Then, the kids behind Chee sped past her. They laughed, looked back at her, and said, "Hey, little kid, you're so short. Ha, ha."

Chee didn't say a word. She remembered the crying little boy outside a few moments earlier. Chee looked straight ahead, stood as tall as she could, and walked into her classroom. "I'm not playing their game," Chee thought.

Questions for Discussion

Say, "Let's talk about the different ways Chee and the little boy handled teasing. We'll talk about some skills to follow when you're being teased." Write the skills on the chalkboard or a flip chart as your students respond.

1. Tell what the teasers in this story said and did.

   laughed, called the victim names like sissy and crybaby

2. Teasers want to upset people. Which students in the story looked upset when they were teased? How?

   The little boy cried, argued, and yelled insults at his teasers.

3. Teasing does upset people, but it usually makes the teaser more determined when you look upset. How can you keep teasers from knowing you're upset?

   Keep quiet until you decide how you'll handle the teasing. (Write **Stop! Don't say a word.***)*

4. True or false? Chee looked upset when she was teased.

   false

5. What did Chee need to do after she didn't say a word?

   think of choices (Write **Think of your choices.**

6. What did Chee do after she kept quiet?

   She ignored the teasers. (Write **Ignore the teasing.***)*

7. One way to handle teasing is to agree with the attackers if what they say is really true. What could Chee say to agree with her attackers?

   "That's true. I'm short." (Write **Agree with the teasing or laugh.***)*

8. Name some things that you wouldn't agree with if teasers teased you about it.

   Answers will vary.

9. Another way to handle teasers is to ask sincerely, "Why did you say that?" Why do you think this method might work?

   The teasers might have trouble answering an honest question. (Write **Ask, "Why did you say that?"***)*

10. Some students handle teasing by saying in a friendly way, "I want you to stop. I don't like what you're saying." Why do you think that method might work?

    Teasers see you're not upset; answers will vary. (Write **Say, "I want you to stop."***)*

Social Skills Activities

Skill A

Stop! Don't Say a Word

1. Help students understand the reason some people tease others. Say, "Teasers like to upset people. When people don't become upset, it takes the 'fun' out of teasing." Then ask, "Which actions will make the teaser think you're upset?"

   tattle *yes*

   say nothing *no*

   argue *yes*

   look straight ahead *no*

   shrug it off *no*

   run away *yes*

   cry *yes*

   say, "You're right. I'm short." *no*

Skill B
Think of Your Choices

Ignore the Teasing

1. Teach your students how to ignore. Say, "Here's something you can do to make you stronger than the teaser: Learn to shrug teasing off. It's a way of saying, 'I don't care. It doesn't matter.' "

   Ask for a volunteer to reverse roles with a puppet you are holding. Then say, "The puppet will be you and you will be the teaser. Tell the puppet what a teaser might say."

   Student Volunteer: "You're so skinny."

   Puppet: "I am not."

   Student Volunteer: "You're as skinny as a stick."

   Say, "You can see that I didn't handle that right. I got upset and answered back. This time, I'm going to shrug it off. I'm going to say to myself, 'So what. It makes no difference.' Now, let's try it again."

   Student Volunteer: "You're so skinny."

   Puppet: doesn't say a word, looks straight ahead, holds head high.

   Student Volunteer: (Silent)

   Say, "I just told myself, 'So what, no big deal.' I shrugged it off. That way, the teaser didn't have anything else to say."

   Ask for a volunteer for a second role play, but this time you play the part of the teaser. This time say, "I'll tease you and you practice shrugging it off."

   Puppet: "Man, you're really weird." (Prompt your student with, "Don't say a word. Just shrug it off; look at me like 'no big deal.' ")

   Student Volunteer: Student ignores taunt, is silent, looks straight ahead, with with head held high.

2. Give rules for ignoring. Write these rules on a poster or chalkboard and say, "Here are some rules that will help you remember how to ignore teasing":

   Don't say a word.

   Stand up straight.

   Look the teaser in the eye like you don't care.

   Don't cry, turn around, or run away.

   Say, "When you shrug teasing off, it's the same as saying, 'Sure, whatever; no big deal; I'm above that; I don't even have time to listen to you; I don't care what you're saying; so what?' "

Agree with the Teasing or Laugh

1. Say, "Another way to be in control when you're teased is to agree with the teaser. It usually leaves the teaser with nothing to say."

   Ask for a volunteer to tease you about something you could agree with: gray hair, freckles, wearing glasses, etc.

   Student Volunteer: "Ha, ha, you have freckles."

   You: "You're right, I do."

   Say, "See, I agreed with you and you had nothing else to say."

   Ask for other things students might be able to agree with or laugh about such as making a terrible play during a game; having a broken arm; wearing glasses or braces; being short, tall, skinny; liking to read; or not liking to read.

Ask, "Why Did You Say That?"

1. One way to stop teasing is to ask the teaser, "Why did you say that?" When questioned about motivation, a teaser may have nothing left to say except, "I don't know."

   Try some of the taunts listed above in a role play. This time, let the volunteers answer with, "Why did you say that?"

Say, "I Want You to Stop."

1. Help your students learn to answer their teasers with an "I message." Remind your students that their first response to a teaser is still "Stop!" Then, when your students feel strong enough , they can add, "I want you to stop."

Act out the following situations. You take the part of the teaser in the following situations and have student volunteers respond to your teasing by saying, "I want you to stop."

At dinner, your brother keeps calling you a geek.

Your friend keeps saying you walk as slow as a turtle.

Every day, the girl next door shouts, "Where did you get that weird coat?"

Your sister laughs at you when you mispronounce words.

Additional Activities

Role-Playing

Review the story in this lesson. Then, select one or more of the following role-play activities.

Choose volunteers to play the young boy and the teaser who says the young boy is the worst athlete. Pretend the young boy chooses to shrug off his teaser this time.

Choose volunteers to play Chee and the teaser that tells Chee she's short. Pretend that Chee chooses to laugh and agree with her teasers.

Choose volunteers to play Marci, José, and an older student. Pretend that Marci and José are on the playground when an older student walks by and says their clothes look funny. The older student says their clothes are weird and asks, "Where'd you get them? I want to be sure not to go to that store." Marci and José decide how to handle the teasing by shrugging it off.

Role-Play Feedback

Encourage the rest of your students to give helpful feedback to the students who participated in the role play. Use these questions to stimulate positive feedback:

What did you like about each character's part?

What skills did the young boy use?

What skill did Chee use?

What did the teaser want Marci and José to do?

How could you tell Marci and José were ignoring the teasing?

What other choices could the students who were teased have made?

How could these role plays be different?

Expanding Learning

Use pages 75 and 76 in the Activities Book to help your students

- make good choices for handling teasers
- learn rules for how to ignore teasing

Use pages 174 through 181 in the Picture Book to help your students

- learn what teasing is
- learn why kids tease
- learn how to deal with teasers

Use page 77 in the Activities Book to help your students review the skills for handling teasing. Have your students think of when and how they can practice these skills. For example, they may say

> "I will stop when someone says that I read too much."
>
> "I will say, 'You're right. I do read a lot.' "

Visualization

Have your students get in comfortable positions to relax. Then say, "Close your eyes and imagine staying in control when you are teased.

"You come to school Monday morning with a new haircut. It's shorter than you like, but you know it'll soon grow out. Another student walks up and says, 'Hey, did you get too close to a lawn mower? That's what I call a short haircut. Ha, ha.'

"It hurts when your friend thinks your hair looks funny. But you tell yourself you're not going to let your friend get the best of you. You remember that your hair grows fast so you just laugh and say, 'You're right, it's short.' And you hold your head up and go on, as if it doesn't matter.

"Another friend catches up to you and says, 'Hey, want to play softball after school?' Then, your friend notices your haircut. He says, 'That's a neat haircut!' You smile and say, 'Thanks.' You're glad somebody thinks your haircut is neat. And you're glad you know how to handle teasing."

Lesson 3: When You Need Permission

Skills

A. Ask yourself, "Do I need permission?"

B. Ask yourself, "Who should I ask?"

C. Choose a good time and place.

D. Ask in a friendly way.

Materials

Activities Book:
pages 78 through 80

Picture Book:
pages 182 through 189

Introduction

Asking permission appropriately requires your students to put themselves in the places of others. Your students must consider, for example, how it would feel to have their own belongings used without their permission. In addition, they must also consider reasons those in authority would deny permission. For example, parents may not be able to afford a requested toy or a brother might want to wear the shirt the student wants to borrow.

Knowing how to ask permission is also important. Your students need to learn that a respectful tone of voice will more likely gain permission than whining or nagging.

As your students mature, they might think they don't need to ask permission as often as they did when they were younger. It's true that asking permission for certain activities changes as your students are able to take increasing responsibility. It's important to learn, however, that everyone, even an adult, needs to ask permission sometime. Regardless of one's age, it's always appropriate to ask permission to use other people's things.

Goals

In this lesson, your students will learn the importance of asking permission before acting impulsively or using another person's belongings. The activities will teach your students to

- learn when they need to ask permission
- ask the right people for permission
- learn when, where, and how to ask permission

Preparation

Ask your students, "Do you have some things you wouldn't want others to use without your permission? Tell me about them."

Say, "Sometimes, as you get older, you may feel that it's not necessary to ask permission. But asking permission to use someone else's things is always necessary, no matter how old you are." Ask, "Why do you think it's always important to ask permission to use someone else's things?"

Social Skills Story

Use page 182 in the Picture Book with this story. Ask, "How would you feel if you discovered someone had taken one of your favorite things without your permission? Why?" Say, "José forgot to ask his brother's permission. Listen to this story."

José lifted his brother Carlos's red, blue, and yellow piñata out of a box. José held Carlos's piñata proudly and carried it around the room so all the students could see.

José brought the piñata because his class was learning about Cinco de Mayo, or Fifth of May, a famous date in Mexican history. Mrs. Sahwani explained, "Piñatas are an important part of Cinco de Mayo. It's a day when children break piñatas filled with candies. Then, they scramble to grab the candies that fall to the ground."

When Marci heard about the candies, she became excited. "Will we get to break your piñata, José?" she asked.

José hadn't thought about breaking the piñata. José thought, "If we break Carlos's piñata, he'll kill me." Suddenly, José felt very worried. "I wish I had asked Carlos before I took his piñata," José thought.

But José heard his friends cheer at the possibility of breaking the piñata. "I can't tell them no now," José told himself.

Then, José said, "Yes! Let's break it. That's what piñatas are for!"

He had told Mrs. Sahwani he could bring the piñata to share with the other students. But he hadn't told her it belonged to his big brother. When he thought about his brother, José felt awful. "I'll try not to think about Carlos right now," he thought.

Mrs. Sahwani stood on a chair and hung the piñata from a hook on the ceiling. José watched Mrs. Sahwani fasten the piñata to the hook. The students formed a circle around the piñata. Then, one by one, Mrs. Sahwani blindfolded students with a handkerchief before they tried to break the piñata with a stick.

When it was Marci's turn, she hit the piñata on her very first try. The piñata broke and the candy scattered over the floor. The students squealed and scurried to pick up as much candy as they could.

Chee said to José, "Thanks for bringing your piñata."

José tried to smile. "Sure," José said. But inside he groaned.

José dreaded going home. "What will I tell Carlos?" he wondered.

Questions for Discussion

Say, "José's problem started when he took his brother's piñata without permission. Let's think of some important skills that might help José the next time he needs to ask permission." Write the skills on the chalkboard or a flip chart as your students respond.

1. True or false? It's important to ask permission any time you want to borrow something from someone. Why?

   True. The person might need to use the belongings, or there may be other reasons he wouldn't want someone to use them. (Write **Ask yourself, "Do I need permission?"***)*

2. Why do you think José took his brother's piñata to school without permission?

   José was so excited about the special day that he forgot to ask; José was afraid his brother would say no; he thought his brother wouldn't mind.

3. José asked his teacher for permission to bring the piñata. Was she the right person to ask? Why?

   Yes. José should have asked his teacher for permission to bring the piñata to class. No. He should've asked his brother about taking his piñata. (Write **Ask yourself, "Who should I ask?"***)*

4. Pretend José remembered to ask his brother for permission. He asked when his brother was on the telephone talking to his girlfriend. Was that the best time to ask? Why?

   No. He would have to interrupt his brother's conversation. It's best not to ask when someone is busy. (Write **Choose a good time and place.***)*

5. Pretend that José chose a good time to ask his brother to use the piñata. Show how he could use a friendly tone of voice to say, "May I take your piñata to school?"

   Students will demonstrate asking with a friendly tone of voice. (Write **Ask in a friendly way.***)*

6. Do you think Carlos would have given José permission to take his piñata to school? Why?

   Answers will vary.

7. What do you think José said about the broken piñata when he saw his brother?

   Answers will vary.

8. Why do you think José didn't tell Mrs. Sahwani he shouldn't have the students break the piñata?

   He didn't want to disappoint the students; he may have thought the students would like him better.

Social Skills Activities

Skill A

Ask Yourself, "Do I Need Permission?"

1. Play "May I?" a variation of the old "Mother, May I?" game to practice asking permission appropriately. In this version, your students aren't allowed to do anything without permission. Choose a student to be the leader. The rest of your students must ask the leader's permission for every action. For example, they must ask, "May I open my notebook?" "May I sharpen my pencil?" "May I put my book on my desk?" "May I cough?" The leader responds with "Yes, you may" or "No, you may not."

2. Discuss reasons parents, teachers, or friends might not give permission to use their belongings or to participate in activities. Use the questions on the next page:

Why would parents say no when you ask to visit a friend? *Your parents can't drive you; you need to do homework or chores; they think you've already visited your friend too often; answers will vary.*

Why would a friend say no when you ask to borrow a toy over the weekend? *He's planning to take it with him on a trip; he wants to play with it himself; he has already loaned it to someone else; answers will vary.*

Why would your teacher say no when you ask to draw on the chalkboard? *It would disturb other students; you're behind on your work; answers will vary.*

3. Contrast times when it's necessary or unnecessary to ask permission. Say, "Would you need to ask permission to do these things? Answer yes or no."

At School

You need to call your mom. *yes*

You need to open your math book to do your work. *no*

You need to borrow crayons. *yes*

You're about to be sick and need to get to the restroom quickly. *no*

You need to write your name on your art project for class. *no*

At Home

You want a drink of water. *no*

You want to visit your grandpa. *yes*

You want to read your little sister a story. *no*

You want to eat a piece of your grandma's apple pie. *yes*

You want to invite a friend over. *yes*

At a friend's house

You need to to call your mom. *yes*

You want a drink of water. *yes*

You want to play with a new toy. *yes*

You want to tell your friend, "I like you." *no*

Skill B

Ask Yourself, "Who Should I Ask?"

1. Say, "Let's think about why you would ask permission from a certain person. Why would you ask

your baby-sitter if you could go next door?"

your neighbor if you could play ball in his yard?"

the grocer if you could return the stale popcorn you bought?"

2. Say, "It's important to think about whose permission you should ask. Listen carefully to the person who gets asked. Clap your hands when you hear a good choice. Shake your head no when the choice is silly. Then, tell who you should ask.

You asked your mom for permission to go to a birthday party. *clap*

You asked your dad for permission to go to a picnic. *clap*

You asked your teacher for permission to use your friend's telephone. *No. Ask your friend.*

You asked the Three Bears for permission to use your dad's hammer. *No. Ask your dad.*

You asked your teacher for permission to go to the school library. *clap*

You asked the Gingerbread Boy for permission to use your sister's book. *No. Ask your sister.*

You asked your friend for permission to wear her sweater. *clap*

You asked the Little Red Hen for permission to spend the night with your friend. *No. Ask your parents.*

You want to ask your sister for permission to listen to her tapes. She is happy because you just brought her a glass of lemonade. *up*

You want to ask your big brother for permission to go with him to the mall. He's angry because you hid his baseball mitt. *down*

Skill C
Choose a Good Time and Place

1. Ask, "Why is it important to choose a good time and place to ask a person's permission?" Then say, "Listen and decide if these are good times to ask permission. Show thumbs-up for good times and thumbs-down for bad times."

   You want to ask your teacher's permission to put your crayons in your cubbie. She just told the class, "Do not get out of your seats." *down*

   You want to ask your mom's permission to buy a new pair of jeans. She has just scolded you for leaving your dirty clothes on the bathroom floor. *down*

   You want to ask your dad for permission to have a friend over. He has just said, "I'm so proud of the good grades you made at school." *up*

Skill D
Ask in a Friendly Way

1. Ask, "Why is it important to ask the other person's permission respectfully?" Point out that it's the other person who owns the possession or who will say yes or no to the activity. The person is more likely to answer yes if you ask in a respectful tone of voice.

2. Say, "Show how you would use a friendly tone of voice and friendly body language to ask permission in these situations. Remember, don't whine, beg, or nag."

   Ask to borrow your friend's pencil.

   Ask to borrow your sister's softball mitt.

   Ask your mom's permission to take your new videotape to school.

Additional Activities

Role-Playing

Review the story in this lesson. Then, select one or more of the following role-play activities.

Choose volunteers to play José and his older brother Carlos. Pretend José asks Carlos if he can take his piñata to school. Encourage your students to decide whether Carlos will say yes or no and how José will respond. Remind the student playing José to use the skills learned for asking permission.

Choose volunteers to play Chee and her grandfather. Pretend Chee asks her grandfather if she may buy something to drink. Remind the student playing Chee to use the skills learned for asking permission.

Choose volunteers to play Jonathan and Mrs. Sahwani. Pretend Jonathan asks Mrs. Sahwani if he may take off his wet shoes. Remind the student playing Jonathan to use the skills learned for asking permission.

Role-Play Feedback

Encourage the rest of your students to give helpful feedback to the role-play volunteers. Use the following questions:

What did you like about each character's part?

What skills did José use for asking permission?

What skills did Chee use for asking permission?

What skills did Jonathan use for asking permission?

How could these role plays be different?

Expanding Learning

Use pages 78 and 79 in the Activities Book to help your students

- practice asking permission
- ask for permission before using someone else's belongings
- choose the appropriate person to ask for permission

Use pages 182 through 189 in the Picture Book to help your students ask permission in a socially effective way.

Use page 80 in the Activities Book to help your students review the skills for asking permission. Have your students suggest when and how they can practice asking permission. For example, they may say

"Do I need to ask Heath if I can borrow his roller blades?"

"I need to ask Heath."

"I will ask Heath during recess."

"I will smile when I ask Heath."

Visualization

Have your students get in comfortable positions to relax. Then say, "Close your eyes and imagine yourself using friendly body language and a friendly tone of voice to ask permission.

"Your best friend told you about a good video he bought. He borrowed a video from you last week so you think he won't mind letting you borrow his video. You decide to think of a good time to ask him. Every day, you walk home from school together. So you decide that today after school will be a good time to ask if you may borrow his video.

"When you start walking home, you smile and say in a friendly way, 'Say, that video you told me about sounds good. Would you mind if I borrow it this weekend?' Your friend says, 'Sure, I'm going to be gone all weekend anyway. I'll get it for you when we get to my house.' You smile and say thank you. You're glad you know how to ask permission."

Lesson 4: When You're Wrong

Skills

A. Stop! Ask yourself, "Was I wrong?"

B. Say, "Yes, I was wrong."

C. Accept the consequences.

D. Show that you feel bad about it.

E. Tell how you'll act next time.

Materials

Activities Book:
pages 81 through 83

Picture Book:
pages 190 through 197

Introduction

Why don't students admit their mistakes? First, admitting mistakes isn't an easy skill to learn. Your students will acquire this skill gradually as they learn to balance self-interest with the rights of others.

Second, it's not easy to accept blame. It's easier for your students to shift blame to others. For example, students can remain blameless if they convince parents and teachers that someone should have reminded them ("You didn't tell me"), didn't explain it well enough ("I didn't know where the mop was"), or wasn't fair ("I always have to do more than others"). Weaknesses of adults can even make the student's failure okay ("The teacher's desk is messy, too. Why do I have to clean mine?").

It's important for your students to learn to accept consequences for their actions. Students who are able to act responsibly, even when they're wrong, learn that punishment might be lessened when they go ahead and admit their mistakes. Your students will also understand that mistakes can be opportunities to learn. After all, that's what growing up is all about.

Goals

In this lesson, your students will practice admitting mistakes and accepting the consequences for their mistakes. The activities will teach your students to

- calmly accept results of behavior
- sincerely apologize when they're wrong
- show that their mistake makes them feel bad
- understand that everyone makes mistakes and they must accept responsibility for the consequences of their mistakes

Preparation

Use everyday situations to lead your students to accept blame when they try to shift responsibility to others. For example, encourage the student who says, "My parents forgot to sign my paper" to reword the sentence and say, "I forgot to get my paper signed." Help your students find satisfaction in being responsible.

Communicate expectations clearly and simply so that your students can learn what they need to do and what the consequences will be if they don't.

Point out that things that happen after we have done something are called *consequences.* Say, "People who don't think about consequences could get in trouble. For example, if you ate a piece of cake that was for the school cake walk, you might have to use your allowance to buy another cake. That's because you didn't think about what could happen in the future if you behaved in a certain way."

Then ask, "What consequences follow good actions, such as being kind to others, listening to your friends, or helping someone who is ill?"

Say, "Everything that happens has a cause. When we do good things, like finishing our schoolwork, there is a good effect, like learning something or getting a good grade."

Social Skills Story

Use page 190 in the Picture Book with this story. Ask, "Should you think of the consequences before or after you do something? Why?" Then say, "One day, Mark didn't think about the consequences of what he was doing. Listen to this story."

It was Mark's job to feed and water his dog, Pal, every morning before school. Every morning, however, Mark's mother had to remind him. Many times she even had to feed Pal herself. Though this made her angry enough to take Mark's allowance away, Mark kept forgetting to feed Pal.

One morning, when Mark and his mom were driving to school, his mom asked, "Did you feed Pal?"

"Yeah," Mark said. But to himself, Mark thought, "I forgot again."

"That's good, Mark," said his mom. "Pal depends on you."

"Yeah," he said. "Pal is a great dog." Then Mark thought, "I wish I had given Pal his food and water."

Mark's mom just kept talking about Pal. Mark began to worry.

"It's a good thing you filled up Pal's water bowl, Mark. He needs water in the hot sun to keep from getting sick or even dying."

"Yeah," mumbled Mark as he got out of the car. "Bye, Mom."

Mark's mom went home and gave Pal some water and food. Her phone rang. It was Mrs. Sahwani.

"Mrs. Carpenter," said Mrs. Sahwani. "Something seems to be bothering Mark. Would you talk to him?"

Then, Mark got on the phone. "Mom, could you see if Pal is okay?" he said sadly. "I hate to tell you this, but I didn't feed Pal this morning. I feel awful. I know what can happen to Pal if I don't feed him, so I'll never forget again."

Questions for Discussion

Say, "Mark really meant it when he admitted his mistake to his mom. Let's see if we can decide on skills that helped Mark take responsibility for his mistake." Write the skills on the chalkboard or a flip chart as your students respond.

1. What was Mark's mistake?

   He forgot to give food and water to his dog.

2. Why do you think Mark kept forgetting about his dog?

   Answers will vary.

3. What helped Mark decide he was wrong in forgetting to feed his dog?

   He thought about what a good friend Pal had been; he thought how sad he would feel if Pal got sick or died because he didn't give him water and food. (Write **Stop! Ask yourself, "Was I wrong?"***)*

4. Did Mark admit he had made a mistake? How did he do it?

   Yes. He told his mother he had told a lie; he was worried about Pal because he really hadn't given him water and food that morning. (Write **Say, "Yes, I was wrong."***)*

5. Could the real consequences of Mark's mistake be serious? Why?

   Yes. Without food and water, especially on hot days, Pal could get sick or die. (Write **Accept the consequences.***)*

6. Mark sounded sad when he admitted he was wrong. Why is it a good idea to show someone that you feel bad about a mistake?

   That way, the other person knows you are sincere. (Write **Show that you feel bad about it.***)*

7. How did Mark act after he admitted his mistake?

   He promised himself he'd take care of Pal. (Write **Tell how you'll act next time.***)*

8. Is it important to change the way you are behaving after you admit your mistake? Why?

   Yes. People will believe you next time; people will know you learned something.

9. What do you think Mark learned about consequences and responsibility?

   Answers will vary.

Social Skills Activities

Skill A

Stop! Ask Yourself, "Was I Wrong?"

1. Ask, "How well do you admit your mistakes?" Draw a line across the chalkboard. At the left end put a circle and say, "This circle is for people who never say 'I was wrong.' They always blame someone else. They say things like, 'I didn't do it,' 'I forgot,' or 'He made me do it.' These people get into a lot of trouble because they keep making mistakes."

   At the right end of the line, draw another circle. Say, "This circle is for people who worry about every little thing. When these people make a mistake they worry too much. Perhaps they cry a long time and think they are terrible people because they weren't perfect. They need to remember that it's normal to make mistakes now and then. Then, they would feel better about themselves."

   In the middle, draw a star. Say, "This star is for people who admit their mistakes." Explain that these people know it's okay to make a few mistakes. They accept the consequences for their mistakes and try not to keep on making the same mistakes again. Most of the time they try hard not to hurt others. Usually they feel good about themselves.

Have your students discuss where they would fall on the chart you have made to indicate how well they think they admit their mistakes.

Skill B

Say, "Yes, I Was Wrong."

1. Your students have daily opportunities to see the relationship between cause and effect. Remind them of the cause/effect principle as often as possible, especially in conflict situations in which students tend not to see how their own behavior has affected others.

   Discuss the effects the following behaviors cause. Ask, "What consequences do you think will follow these actions?"

   You disobey the teacher.

   You don't do your jobs at home.

   You tease your best friend and call her a bad name.

   Someone calls you a name.

   You grab your sister's rattle and she cries.

   You forget your lunch.

   You play with matches.

2. Discuss possible causes of good effects. Say, "There are many good things that happen because of what we do. Tell some possible causes for these good things":

   Your brother says, "I like you."

   You get a good grade on a test.

   Your mom says, "I'm glad to see behavior like that."

   Your teacher says, "The class may have an extra ten minutes at recess."

   You get a smiley face on your homework paper.

   Your dad says, "That shows you're growing up."

Skill C

Accept the Consequences

1. In each of the following situations, have your students take the role of an adult. Say, "What consequences would you give in each situation?"

   Pretend you're the parent. Your daughter talked to you in a rude tone, went to her room, and slammed her door.

   Pretend you're the teacher. A student is constantly late for school.

   Pretend you're the principal. A boy started a fight at school. Then he yelled, "I didn't do it" at the principal.

   Pretend you're the store owner. A girl takes candy from the counter without paying.

Skill D

Show that You Feel Bad About It

1. Say, "What could you do to show the person you feel bad in each situation?"

   You come home one hour late from school. What could you do to show your mom you feel bad about your mistake?

   You forgot your book for the fourth time. What could you do to show your teacher you feel bad about your mistake?

You play ball in the park and break a flowerpot on a nearby porch. What could you do to show the home owner you feel bad about your mistake?

Skill E
Tell How You'll Act Next Time

1. Point out that everyone makes mistakes sometimes. Ask, "Can you think of anything good about making mistakes?" Say, "The good thing about mistakes is they help us learn more about the world." Then tell the following story.

   Laura went to a new friend's house to play after school, but she didn't call the baby-sitter to tell her where she was. When Laura didn't come home at her usual time, the baby-sitter called the friends Laura usually plays with. When the friends told the baby-sitter that Laura wasn't at their homes, the baby-sitter was really worried so she called Laura's parents at work and she called the police. When Laura came home, she saw the baby-sitter and her parents crying.

   Laura's parents punished her. She wasn't allowed to play with her friends after school for one month.

   Laura missed her friends. After her punishment, she told her parents that she'll remember to call home if she goes to a friend's house after school.

   Ask, "Have you ever learned anything from a mistake you made? Do you think it's important to tell the person you will try to avoid doing the same thing again? Why?"

Additional Activities

Role-Playing

Review the story in this lesson. Then, select one or more of the role-play activities.

Choose volunteers to play Mark and his mom. Pretend that Mark's mom takes away Mark's allowance because he keeps forgetting to feed and water his dog. Remind Mark to use the skills for when you're wrong.

Choose volunteers to play a father and a son. Pretend that the son lied to the father about playing with matches. Have the father give a consequence to the son. Remind the person playing the son to show that he feels bad about lying.

Choose volunteers to play a mother and a daughter. Pretend the daughter was supposed to rake the leaves before she went to the movie, but she didn't. The daughter said she was ready to go to the movie. Have the mother give a consequence to the daughter. Remind the person playing the daughter to accept the consequence.

Choose volunteers to play Janine and Valesia. Pretend Janine took Valesia's wind-up toy home without asking. Janine feels bad and is afraid Valesia won't like her when she finds out. Remind the person playing Janine to use the skills for when you're wrong.

Role-Play Feedback

Encourage the rest of your students to give helpful feedback to the role-play volunteers. Use the following questions:

What did you like about each character's part?

What skills did Mark use?

What was the son's consequence?

What was the daughter's consequence?

What skills did Janine use?

How could these role plays be different?

Expanding Learning

Use pages 81 through 82 in the Activities Book to help your students

- choose ways to accept consequences
- discuss behavior that can ensure good consequences
- decide ways to admit mistakes appropriately

Use pages 190 through 197 in the Picture Book to help your students increase their skills in handling situations when they're wrong.

Use page 83 in the Activities Book to help your students review the skills learned for when they're wrong. Have your students list times when they can practice these skills. For example, they may say

"I was wrong to have pushed Melanie in the line."

"I did push Melanie."

"I will go to the end of the line."

"I will apologize."

"Next time, I'll keep my hands to myself."

Visualization

Have your students get in comfortable positions to relax. Then say, "Close your eyes and imagine yourself knowing what to do when you make a mistake.

"Pretend you're running down the school hallway with your friend. Running inside the building is against the rules. You just aren't thinking. As you and your friend turn the corner, you run into the principal. She looks at you sternly and tells you to go to her office. You feel awful as you walk to the office with your friend. You have to sit in a chair outside the principal's office for a few minutes. You worry about the consequences of your mistake.

"First, your friend goes in the office. Later, it's your turn. When you go into the principal's office, she looks at you and says, 'You know the rule about no running in the hallway. Now, you must stay after school for 20 minutes.'

"In a polite voice you admit you were wrong. You say, 'Yes, I did it. I just wasn't thinking about the rule. I'll stay after school, and I won't run in the hall again.' The principal smiles at you and says, 'I'm glad to have students who know how to accept the consequences when they break a rule. You may use my phone to call your mother so she'll know you'll be late today.'

"You feel glad that you know everyone makes mistakes sometimes. You're glad you know how to admit mistakes and how to accept the consequences."

Lesson 5: When You're Not Wrong

Skills

A. Stop! Listen to the person blaming you.

B. Ask yourself, "Did I do it?"

C. If yes, apologize and make up for it.

D. If no, explain calmly that you didn't do it.

Materials

Activities Book:
pages 84 through 86

Picture Book:
pages 198 through 205

Introduction

Many students have difficulty dealing with false accusations. They may lash out angrily, say "No way!," or refuse to talk or listen. These behaviors might imply guilt and they won't solve the problem.

Self-control is difficult, but it's especially important when your students are blamed for something they didn't do. It's hard to stay calm in response to a false accusation, but a calm response could signify innocence.

Understanding an accusation is the key to responding calmly, especially when you've been wrongly accused. Is the accuser jumping to conclusions? Does the accuser have all the information? Why is the accusation being made? Both listening to and analyzing an accusation will help your students take an objective stance that enhances self-control.

Everyone has had to deal with a false accusation at some time. Dealing with false accusations by calming down before you respond is an important aspect of this social skill. Learning to handle strong angry feelings helps your students interact more confidently in their relationships with peers and adults.

Goals

This lesson will provide opportunities to help your students practice self-control when they're blamed for something they didn't do. The activities will teach your students to

- listen to the accuser
- act appropriately when being accused

Preparation

Think of your students' communication skills. Which students have difficulty explaining their innocence, even if they truly aren't to blame? Which students call names, cry, or yell in response to an accusation?

With your students, discuss feelings associated with being blamed for something you didn't do. Say, "Suppose a student told the principal you took his things from the Lost and Found at school. You didn't take anything, but you had to go to the principal's office. How would you feel? How could you let the principal know you didn't do it?"

Then ask, "Why is it important to handle your anger when someone blames you for something you didn't do?" Point out that if you get angry and yell, you might look guilty.

Social Skills Story

Use page 198 in the Picture Book with this story. Say, "When you know you didn't do something you've been blamed for, you have no reason to get upset. Try to think about what the person is saying to you. That way you can stay calm. Let's see what Marci did when she was blamed for something she didn't do. Listen to this story."

Marci looked at the note in her hand as she walked down the school hallway. It said *See Mrs. Huggs first thing Monday morning!* "This looks important," Marci thought.

Marci felt a little worried. She wondered, "Why do I have to go to the library? I hope I'm not in trouble."

Then, Marci had a happy thought. "Mrs. Huggs is always smiling. Maybe she has a new book for me."

Marci opened the library door and walked toward Mrs. Huggs. When Marci reached Mrs. Huggs's desk, she said, "Hi, Mrs. Huggs."

Mrs. Huggs looked up from her cluttered desk. When she saw it was Marci, she frowned.

"Uh-oh," thought Marci. "I'm in trouble."

"Marci," Mrs. Huggs said seriously. "I checked my computer records and saw that you didn't return the book, *Blueberries for Sal.*" Mrs. Huggs wasn't smiling. Her voice was friendly, though. "You should have returned it three weeks ago, Marci! You'll have to pay for this book if you've lost it."

Marci felt like crying, but she didn't. She just listened and thought about what Mrs. Huggs was saying.

Then, Marci took a deep breath and said in a friendly voice, "Mrs. Huggs, I did bring *Blueberries for Sal* back. I put the book on your counter."

Marci continued, "Yesterday, I saw a boy on the bus with the same book. I think it was the same book because it had a red mark across the front just like mine did."

"Do you know the boy's name?" asked Mrs. Huggs.

"No," said Marci, "but I know he's in Mr. Bohnsack's classroom. I'll go to Mr. Bohnsack's room to get the book."

Questions for Discussion

Say, "Marci stayed calm when Mrs. Huggs blamed her for the lost library book. Let's talk about the story and discover some important skills for staying calm after you've been blamed for something you didn't do." Write the skills on the chalkboard or a flip chart as your students respond.

1. What was Mrs. Huggs's problem?

   She was missing a library book.

2. What was Marci's problem?

   She was blamed for not having returned her library book.

3. What do you think had happened to the book?

   Maybe Marci had put the book on the counter, but hadn't waited to check it in properly. Then, a boy had picked up the book without checking it out.

4. How did Marci feel when Mrs. Huggs accused her of not returning the library book?

   like crying

5. How do you think Marci kept from crying?

   Answers will vary.

6. What important thing did Marci do when she heard Mrs. Huggs say, "You should have returned the book three weeks ago"?

   Marci listened to Mrs. Huggs. (Write **Stop! Listen to the person blaming you.***)*

7. Do you think Marci asked herself, "Did I do it?"

   Probably. She thought about what she had done when she brought the book back. (Write **Ask yourself, "Did I do it?"***)*

8. Suppose Marci had lost the book. What do you think she should do?

   apologize and pay for the book (Write **If yes, apologize and make up for it.***)*

9. Was it a good idea for Marci to explain what she thought had happened to the book? Why?

   Yes. So she didn't get in trouble. (Write **If no, explain calmly that you didn't do it.***)*

10. What do you think Mrs. Huggs would have done if Marci had cried, stamped her foot, and walked away?

    Answers will vary.

Social Skills Activities

Skill A

Stop! Listen to the Person Blaming You

1. Discuss with your students that strong feelings can keep you from listening and responding appropriately. Say, "You might feel angry because you think it's not fair when someone blames you for something you didn't do. You might say to yourself, 'That's not fair!' You might be very angry and feel like saying, 'No way! You're crazy if you think I did that!' Or you might feel so angry that you feel like shouting, stamping your foot, and walking away. These feelings are okay to have, but hitting and fighting aren't effective ways to deal with being wrongly blamed." Ask your students to explain why. *Responding in an angry way will make them look guilty. Also, it's not okay to hit in anger.*

2. Write these three situations on the chalkboard: cheating at a game, stealing a toy, hitting a small child. Say, "Pretend that someone accused you of doing one of

these things that you didn't do. How would you react?"

3. Ask, "Why is it important to listen when someone is blaming you?" Point out that the person might not have all the information. Then, give the following examples and ask your students to tell possible information the other person might not have.

   You took the paintbrushes from the art room! *Examples of information needed: I haven't been in the art room this week. I saw another person take a paintbrush. There were no paintbrushes in the art room today. I couldn't find one, either.*

   You didn't clean the counter after making a snack. *Examples of information needed: I did clean the counter. Brother (or sister) made a snack after I did. Perhaps the brother (or sister) didn't clean it. I didn't make a snack today.*

   You made prank calls to my house last night. *Examples of information needed: I didn't call your house. I was at the ball game all evening. Our phone is broken. Someone made prank calls to my house, too.*

4. Suggest that another reason to listen is to ask a question to clarify the accusation. Say, "What question might help to clear up these accusations?"

   You left a mess on the porch. *What is on the front porch?*

   You left the faucet running. *Which faucet was running? When was it running?*

   You told a lie about me. *What was the lie? How do you know there was a lie told about you?*

Skill B

Ask Yourself, "Did I Do It?"

1. Ask your students why it's important to ask themselves whether or not they did what they were accused of. Point out that asking themselves this question will give them time to think about the accusation. Thinking about the accusation could help them cool off and choose a good response.

   Turn the accusation process around. Ask, "What would be important to do if you accused someone else of something, such as copying or telling a secret?"

   Point out that it's important to have the right information before blaming someone. Ask your students what information they would need before accusing

   a kid of taking candy from a store

   another student of cheating during a game

   a friend of taking your crayons

   a family member of using your toothbrush

Skill C

If Yes, Apologize and Make Up for It

1. Ask your students why it's important to apologize if you're accused of something that you did. Tell your students that it's important to say they're sorry in a sincere way and to tell the person how they plan to change their behavior. Then, have them practice apologizing in the following situations. Remind them to show that they're sincere.

   Your mom accused you of leaving your dirty clothes in the middle of the floor.

   Your grandma accused you of drinking some of the punch she was saving for a party.

Your friend accused you of taking her new smelly stickers.

Your friend accused you of cheating at checkers.

Skill D

If No, Explain Calmly that You Didn't Do It

1. Ask, "Why isn't it good to yell or call a person names after he blames you for something you didn't do?" Explain that the other person won't listen to you and the problems won't get solved.

2. Ask, "Why is it important to explain politely that you didn't do something you're blamed for?" Then, read this situation: "Pretend that a student told the principal you took something of his from the Lost and Found yesterday. Show thumbs-up when you hear answers that could help clear things up and show thumbs-down for answers that won't help."

   "I didn't take it. I was looking through the Lost and Found with Mark who lost his lunch box. Mark knows I didn't take it." *up*

   You refuse to talk. You just shake your head and walk away. *down*

   Your face gets red and you say angrily, "I would never do something like that. He lied!" *down*

   "I didn't do it, but I may know who did. I saw someone put something in his pocket when he left the Lost and Found." *up*

   "I didn't do it. I was absent from school yesterday." *up*

Additional Activities

Role-Playing

Review the story in this lesson. Then, select one or more of the role-play activities.

Choose volunteers to play Marci and the boy who had the same library book she had. Pretend that Marci accuses the boy of taking the book without checking it out. Pretend that the boy did take the book without checking it out. Remind the student playing the boy to apologize.

Choose volunteers to play Karen and her sister, Maria. Pretend Karen accused Maria of using her hairbrush, but Maria didn't use it. Maria remembers seeing their brother brushing his hair in the bathroom yesterday. Remind the student playing Maria to use the skills for when you're not wrong.

Choose volunteers to play Maurice and Joel. Pretend that Maurice accuses Joel of eating his cookie. Joel did eat Maurice's cookie. Remind the student playing Joel to apologize.

Role-Play Feedback

Encourage the rest of your students to give helpful feedback to the role-play volunteers. Use the following questions:

What did you like about each character's part?

How did the boy apologize?

What skills did Maria use when she wasn't wrong?

How did Joel apologize?

How could these role plays be different?

Expanding Learning

Use pages 84 and 85 in the Activities Book to help your students

- listen carefully to accusations
- answer accusers calmly
- discuss how having a good reputation makes them believable

Use pages 198 through 205 in the Picture Book to help your students respond appropriately when blamed unjustly.

Use page 86 in the Activities Book to help your students review the skills for when you're not wrong. Have your students suggest when and how they can practice these skills. For example, they may suggest

"I will listen to my big sister when she blames me for playing with her toys."

"Did I play with her Nintendo?"

"Yes, I'm sorry. I played with your Nintendo."

"I didn't play with your Nintendo."

Visualization

Have your students relax and get in comfortable positions. Then say, "Close your eyes and imagine yourself answering calmly.

"A boy accused you of tearing a page out of a library book. You listen quietly while he says, 'I saw you tear a page out of a book. You're going to get in big trouble.' You know you didn't do it and you wonder why he would blame you. But you feel a little angry at the boy for blaming you.

"So you take a deep breath and look at the boy. Then, you say in a friendly way, 'You've made a mistake. You saw me tear a paper, but it wasn't a page from the book.' The kid just looks down and mumbles, 'Well, I thought it was the book,' and walks away. You're glad you didn't let yourself answer in an angry way. You're glad you know what to do when someone blames you for something you didn't do."

Being Responsible

A teacher once described her surprise and sadness at finding that one of her second graders had given away her entire lunch because other children asked for parts of it. It's critical for such a child to learn that it's okay to say no in order to be responsible and look out for herself. She could learn, for example, to say in a friendly, firm way, "I can't give away my lunch because I need it for myself."

In order to be socially responsible, students must recognize they have needs, value their needs as important, and recognize and value the needs of others. It's important for your students to be able to express and meet their own needs without violating the needs of others.

The lessons in Unit 5 will help your students develop responsible relationships through practice with the following social language skills:

Lesson 1: Speaking up in a firm, confident manner when they believe things aren't fair.

Lesson 2: Taking action to deal with the hurt of being left out instead of withdrawing, pouting, or continuing to feel hurt.

Lesson 3: Communicating positively during competition by winning graciously and losing with dignity.

Lesson 4: Accepting no for an answer graciously.

Lesson 5: Saying no in a firm, kind way.

Lesson 6: Working out mutually acceptable solutions during times of conflict with others.

Lesson 1: Complaining When Things Aren't Fair

Skills

A. Ask yourself, "What's the problem?"

B. Tell the right person.

C. Choose a good time and place.

D. Tell what you want to happen.

Materials

Activities Book:
page 88 through 91

Picture Book:
page 206 through 213

Introduction

A sense of fairness develops throughout the elementary school years so that by the time students are nine years old, they have a strong understanding of what's fair and what's not. Expressing complaints can be difficult, even for adults. Students, however, can begin to learn ways to speak up in a confident manner when they believe things aren't fair. It's important for your students to express their complaints in a confident, calm way when they feel things are unfair.

Goals

In this lesson, your students will learn when and how to complain when things aren't fair. The activities will help your students

- learn to talk to the people who are bothering them
- discuss differences between fair and unfair complaints
- learn who to complain to
- learn good and poor times to complain

Preparation

With your students, discuss reasons they may be treated unfairly.

Have your students tell you things their parents let their younger brothers and sisters do that they aren't allowed to do. *babies don't have chores, don't share, eat with their fingers; answers will vary*

Have your students list things they'll be allowed to do when they get older that they aren't allowed to do now. *cross a street alone, stay up late, drive cars; answers will vary*

Ask your students to name certain actions that everyone knows aren't fair. *teasing, not taking turns, using toys or belongings without permission, telling secrets, being rude; answers will vary*

Social Skills Story

Use page 206 in the Picture Book with this story. Ask, "Why is it important to complain without making someone mad at you?" Then say, "If you don't tell others what they're doing bothers you, they'll keep on doing it. Something bothered Jonathan and the other students. Let's see what happened. Listen to this story."

One Monday morning, Jonathan leaned forward to whisper to Marci, "There goes Mark again, choosing volleyball for free play." Every Monday, Mrs. Sahwani allowed one student in Room 14 to choose a game that the whole class would play. Whenever Mrs. Sahwani chose Mark, he always wanted to play volleyball.

Marci turned toward Jonathan, rolled her eyes, and groaned. "No fair," she whispered.

Mrs. Sahwani told the students to line up for free play. Then, she smiled at Mark and said, "You may get the volleyball, Mark."

Jonathan was glad it was time for free play. He liked to play volleyball, but soccer was his favorite game. As Jonathan waited his turn, he thought, "Mrs. Sahwani always lets Mark choose the game for free play. I'd like to choose soccer sometime."

On the following Monday, Jonathan and Marci talked before school about Mrs. Sahwani always asking Mark to choose the free play game. Marci said angrily, "It's not fair that Mrs. Sahwani always does what Mark wants."

Then, José walked up and said, "What's up?"

"Oh, we're talking about Mark, the teacher's pet," said Jonathan.

José said, "Yeah, what will 'Marky Boy' choose for free play this week?"

When Jonathan saw that everybody was feeling angry about it, he said, "Let's go talk to Mrs. Sahwani."

"Not me," said José.

"Not me, either," said Marci. "She'll get mad at us!"

Jonathan said, "You guys are right. We'd probably just get in trouble."

Questions for Discussion

Say, "Jonathan and his friends need to learn skills for complaining when things aren't fair. Write the skills on the chalkboard or a flip chart as your students respond.

1. True or false? Having a tantrum is a good way to handle your angry feelings when things don't seem fair. Why?

   False. It's best to tell about your anger early, before it builds up into a tantrum.

2. What was the problem in this story?

   The students weren't getting a fair chance to choose the games for free play. (Write **Ask yourself, "What's the problem?"***)*

3. What game did Jonathan want to play?

   soccer

4. It's important to go to the right person to complain. Would Mrs. Sahwani have been the right person? Why?

   Yes. She was the one who could change things. (Write **Tell the right person.***)*

5. It's also important to choose a good time and place. When should Jonathan talk to Mrs. Sahwani if he were to complain?

   after school, at recess (Write **Choose a good time and place.***)*

6. What would be a bad time for Jonathan to talk to Mrs. Sahwani? Why?

   Answers will vary.

7. What would Mrs. Sahwani do if Jonathan complained by throwing a tantrum?

   Answers will vary.

8. Pretend you're Jonathan. What would you say to Mrs. Sahwani to let her know what you want to happen?

   "Mark seems to always get called on to choose a game. I'd like to choose, too." Answers will vary. (Write **Tell what you want to happen.***)*

Social Skills Activities

Skill A

Ask Yourself, "What's the Problem?"

1. Help your students learn to successfully complain about their own problems. Tell them they don't have to complain about something that bothers someone else. Say, "For example, if you don't like someone's shoes, you don't say anything. You don't complain to the person and say, 'I don't like your shoes.' " Have your students choose the situation they would complain about in each of the following pairs.

   You complain that you don't like your sister's haircut.

   You complain that you don't like your own haircut.

   Your brother has his own room. You complain that his room is messy.

   Your brother shares a room with you. You complain that he left his dirty clothes on your bed.

   You complain to your friend that he keeps using your crayons and not putting them back.

   You complain to your friend that he keeps using another person's crayons and not putting them back.

   You complain to your mom that your little sister is yelling and acting silly at the park.

   You complain to your mom that your little sister is yelling and acting silly in the house, bothering you while you study.

Skill B

Tell the Right Person

1. Use the following situation to help students choose an appropriate person to complain to.

   Your friend took your story, copied it, and handed it in to the teacher. When he got the story back from the teacher, it had a gold star on it.

   What would happen if you complained to

   the person sitting next to you?
   your mom and dad?
   a group of kids on the playground?
   the principal?
   the teacher?
   the student who took your story?

2. Explain to your students that sometimes it's easier to complain in writing than to complain by talking. Help those students who can write organize their thoughts in the form of a letter and send it to the right person. Use these guidelines:

   Make the letter brief.
   Make it friendly.
   Tell what's wrong.
   Tell what you want to happen.

   Write this example on the chalkboard:

   Dear Older Sis,

   Last week, I saw you take 50¢ from my purse. It's hard for me to write this letter, but I feel very upset. I want you to return my money. Next time, I want you to ask me before you take anything from my purse.

   Your sister,

   Jenny

Skill C

Choose a Good Time and Place

1. Present this situation: Your friend has been putting her things in your cubbie because it's close to her desk. Now it's getting full, so there's no room for your things. What will happen if you complain to her

   when she's playing a group game at recess?

   when she's talking to the teacher?

   when she's eating lunch with you?

   when you're sitting next to each other in a car?

   when she's about to put her glue in your cubbie and you're standing nearby?

   when you're standing in front of the building before school?

Skill D

Tell What You Want to Happen

1. Say, "When we complain, we need to tell the person who's making us complain what we want to happen. Let's practice asking for what we want."

   Make a want list. Begin at the top of a page with the words, "I want . . . ." Have younger students draw pictures of all the things they want to have or do when they get older.

   Then, ask them to select one thing they can make happen right now. Have them list or draw all the things they can do to make it happen. Finally, have them draw a picture of themselves enjoying this goal.

2. Say, "When a person is *confident*, he seems to know what he wants. He stands tall and talks in a strong voice. Use a confident, friendly tone of voice and polite words when you're going to complain."

Have your students show thumbs-up after you read the confident complaint and thumbs-down after the angry complaint. Then, ask volunteers to role-play the confident complaints.

Your brother is playing music too loudly while you're talking on the phone. You'd like to be able to hear your friend.

You yell, "Turn down your stupid music! I can't hear a thing!" *down*

You lay the phone down, go to your brother and say, "I'm having a hard time hearing on the phone. Could you please turn your music down?" *up*

Your friend interrupts you every time you talk with her. It really bothers you. You'd like to have a friendly conversation.

You choose a good time and say, "I don't want to hurt your feelings, but it really bothers me that you interrupt me when we're talking." *up*

The next time she interrupts you, you yell, "You creep! I'm sick of being interrupted every time I open my mouth. Get lost!" *down*

You don't like the clothes your parents choose for you and you would like to dress the way you want.

You tell yourself to forget about it because they might get mad. *down*

You say, "Thanks for buying clothes for me, but I'd feel better if I could start picking out some of my own clothes now." *up*

Additional Activities

Role-Playing

Review the story in this lesson. Then, select volunteers to role-play one or more of the following role-play activities.

Choose volunteers to play Jonathan and Mrs. Sahwani. Pretend that Jonathan complains about Mark choosing the class game every week. Remind the student playing Jonathan to use the skills learned for complaining when things aren't fair.

Choose volunteers to play Tim and Benjamin. Pretend Tim keeps using Benjamin's scissors without permission. Remind the student playing Benjamin to tell Tim what he wants to happen.

Choose volunteers to play Nick and the store clerk. Pretend Nick bought a new toy with his savings, but the toy doesn't work when he gets it home. Pretend the clerk won't let Nick return the toy. Remind the student playing Nick to use the skills for complaining when things aren't fair.

Role-Play Feedback

Encourage the rest of your students to give helpful feedback to the role-play volunteers. Use the following questions:

What did you like about each character's part?

What skills did Jonathan use?

What did Benjamin say to Tim that he wanted to happen?

What skills did Nick use?

How could these role plays be different?

Expanding Learning

Use pages 88 through 90 in the Activities Book to help your students

- know when it's fair to complain
- complain in a confident way
- go to the right person to complain

Use pages 206 through 213 in the Picture Book to help your students complain appropriately.

Use page 91 in the Activities Book to help your students review the skills for complaining when things aren't fair. Have your students suggest when and how they could practice these skills. For example, they may say

"The problem is that Hillary pushes me in line."

"I will tell Hillary."

"I will tell her next time we're walking home from school alone."

"I will say, 'I feel like I'm going to fall when you push me in line. I want you to please keep your hands to yourself when we're in line.' "

Visualization

Have your students get in comfortable positions to relax. Then say, "Close your eyes and imagine yourself talking in a friendly but serious way to your friend who has been bugging you.

"Your friend keeps talking to you in class, but you're the one who usually gets in trouble. You see your friend after school, go up to her, and start a friendly conversation. Then, you say politely, 'I don't want to hurt your feelings, but it really embarrasses me when you talk to me in class and the teacher yells at me.'

"Your friend listens and tells you she understands how that could really bug you. She says she will stop. You smile at each other and you ask her if she can come to your house for cookies and milk. You're glad you know how to complain in a nice way."

Lesson 2: When You're Left Out

Skills

A. Admit it hurts.

B. Tell yourself, "Awful doesn't last forever."

C. Do something about it.

Ask to join in.

Ask why you were left out.

Find a new friend.

Get into another fun activity.

Materials

Activities Book:
pages 92 through 95

Picture Book:
pages 214 through 221

Introduction

Everyone has experienced some kind of rejection. Students feel rejection when they're not chosen to answer the teacher's question, left out by a good friend, or picked last by the team captain.

Rejection can't be changed, but the way your students feel about and respond to rejection can. That's the goal of this lesson. Communication is important to attaining this goal. After all, noncommunicative solutions, such as withdrawing and pouting, are self-defeating. Good communicative behavior is required to join the group, talk to the people who left them out, or find other friends or alternative activities.

Responsible inner language is also important. The student who tells himself, "This isn't the end of the world. I'm still a good person," can deal with rejection in a healthy way.

Teaching your students to deal with being left out will give them skills they might otherwise have difficulty acquiring. Your students might be surprised to learn that everyone experiences rejection, and most people have difficulty talking about it. Learning about rejection can help your students learn to deal with their own hurt.

Goals

In this lesson, your students will practice dealing responsibly with rejection. The activities will help your students

- deal with their hurt feelings
- take action instead of continuing to feel hurt

Preparation

Encourage helpful responses to being left out by listening to your students' feelings. Explain that everyone faces rejection and feels bad when it happens, but your students can learn not to be devastated. After all, even adults feel bad when their friends forget appointments or don't return their phone calls.

Say, "Raise your hand if you've ever thought to yourself, 'Nobody likes me.' " Allow your students to discuss what caused them to feel like this.

Social Skills Story

Use page 214 in the Picture Book with this story. Introduce your students to the importance of doing something about their feelings when they're left out, instead of continuing to feel hurt or angry. Say, "Mark had a lot of friends, but one day he felt that no one liked him. Listen to this story."

Mark galloped down the school corridor after José, Jonathan, and Bonnie. "Hey, wait for me. I want to sit by you guys on the bus!" Mark yelled.

José turned to talk to Mark, but Jonathan and Bonnie hurried on. José said, "I can't sit by you today, Mark. Bonnie's mom is picking us up and taking us ice skating. See you tomorrow."

Mark stopped running. "Oh . . . see you . . . ," he mumbled.

Mark sadly walked toward the school bus. Mark and José always sat together on the bus. Mark was lonely without his friend. Mark thought, "My friends didn't invite me to skate. Maybe they don't like me. I guess I'm not a good person. No wonder they don't want me." These thoughts made Mark feel even worse.

The bus ride home seemed very long. But finally Mark got home.

"Hey, Mark," called his dad. "Come tell me about your day."

"Oh, my day was okay, Dad, until I started to get on the bus." Mark heaved a big sigh and told his dad about being left out when his friends went ice skating.

Dad said, "You seem to be feeling pretty hurt. I know how you feel. I remember when I was your age. Some days I just wandered around at recess. I felt like no one wanted to play with me. It felt awful."

Mark looked surprised. "Yeah? What did you do?"

Dad said, "After a while, I found a new group of friends."

Mark thought about that, then said, "Maybe that will happen to me."

"Maybe," said Dad. "But maybe your friends didn't mean to leave you out. There might be another reason they didn't invite you. After all, it doesn't mean you're a bad person just because they didn't invite you."

Mark thought about what his dad said. Somehow he didn't feel so awful anymore. Mark said, "As much as I miss my friends, I'll get over it. We'll play together again. Besides, there are other people I can play with, too. Now, I'm going to play a computer game."

Questions for Discussion

Say, "Let's think of some skills to help Mark the next time he's left out." Write the skills on the chalkboard or a flip chart as your students respond.

1. Mark felt awful when he was left out. Was it a good idea for Mark to tell his Dad how he felt? Why?

   Yes. Mark's dad helped Mark feel better. (Write **Admit it hurts.***)*

2. When Mark's feelings were hurt, he told himself mean things, like "I'm not their friend. I'm not even a good person." Does it help Mark to talk to himself like that? Why?

   No. Talking to yourself in a mean way just makes you feel worse; mean things aren't true.

3. Why do you think Bonnie didn't invite Mark to go skating?

   Maybe she could only choose two people; answers will vary.

4. What's something nice Mark could have told himself when he felt left out?

   Answers will vary. (Write **Tell yourself, "Awful doesn't last forever."***)*

5. Why is it important to do something about it when you feel left out?

   You can take charge and help yourself begin to feel better if you choose an action to take; you'll be unhappy if you just sit around thinking about your hurt feelings. (Write **Do something about it.***)*

6. Sometimes you can ask others if you can join in. Would that have been a good choice for Mark? Why?

   Answers will vary. (Write **Ask to join in.***)*

7. Sometimes you're left out by mistake, and it's okay to ask why you were left out. Would that have been a good choice for Mark? Why?

   Answers will vary. (Write **Ask why you were left out.***)*

8. Have you ever been left out by mistake? Tell about it.

   Answers will vary.

9. What choice did Mark's dad make when his childhood friends left him out?

   He found new friends. (Write **Find a new friend.***)*

10. Do you think Mark will need to make new friends, or can he keep José, Jonathan, and Bonnie as friends? Why?

    Answers will vary.

11. What did Mark do about his hurt feelings?

    He talked to his dad; he played a computer game. (Write **Get into another fun activity.***)*

12. Pretend you're Mark talking to yourself after your friends left you. Tell yourself something kind.

    Students will demonstrate.

Social Skills Activities

Skill A

Admit It Hurts

1. Play "Hearts and Band-Aids."[1] Help your students understand that the hurt they feel when they're left out is emotional, not physical. Give each student a Band-Aid and a paper heart. Have him hold up the Band-Aid when you talk about hurting the body. Have him hold up the heart when you talk about hurtful feelings.

[1]Vernon, A. *Thinking, Feeling, Behaving: An Emotional Education Curriculum for Children.* Champaign, IL: Research Press, 1989.

Read the following situations and have your students take turns identifying the kind of hurt you're describing by saying either "It would hurt my feelings" or "It would hurt my body."

You fall on the concrete and skin your knee. *body*

Your grandfather becomes very sick. *feelings*

Your sister says, "Go away and leave me alone." *feelings*

You break your arm on the playground. *body*

Your pet dies. *feelings*

Your friend forgets to come to your party. *feelings*

You bump your forehead on a library shelf. *body*

2. Choose volunteers to tell about a time when they felt rejected. Offer to tell about a time when a parent forgot your meeting or some similar time you experienced being forgotten. Point out that your students can change how they feel by changing what they tell themselves about the situation.

3. Explain to your students that being left out is often unintentional. Guide students to see that being left out happens for many reasons.

   Ask, "Can you think of a time when you ignored someone you care about?" *Perhaps students ignored someone because they felt sick or were worried about something else.*

   Ask, "Can you think of a time when you didn't return someone's call?" *Perhaps students were too busy to call a friend back, didn't get the message, or forgot to return the call.*

   Ask, "Does it mean that someone doesn't like you when she doesn't invite you somewhere? What does it mean?" *It could be a mistake that you weren't invited; maybe she could choose only one or two people; or maybe she's worried about her own problems.*

   Ask, "What if someone doesn't like you? Does that mean you're a bad person?" *Point out that not everyone can like you. After all, there are some people you don't like. You're still a good person.*

Skill B

Tell Yourself, "Awful Doesn't Last Forever."

1. Help your students recognize self put-downs. Draw a sad face on a plain paper bag. Write the following put-downs on slips of paper and put them into the paper bag:

   I'm a dummy.

   I'm worthless.

   My friend doesn't like me.

   I knew my friend didn't like me.

   No wonder they left me out. I'm stupid.

   I don't know how to talk to people.

   Have you or your students take turns reading the put-downs. Say to your students, "These are put-downs. You can give them to other people or to yourself." Then, discuss the feelings these put-downs generate with these questions:

   How did putting yourself down make you feel?

   Have you ever put yourself down?

   Does talking to yourself like this help you? Why?

   How can you stop saying these kinds of things to yourself?

Now, help your students talk to themselves like good friends. Draw a happy face on another plain paper bag and help your students read slips of paper that have these friendly thoughts:

As much as I miss my friend, there are other things I can do.

We'll play together again. It's not such a big deal.

I don't feel wonderful, but I'll get over it.

I feel awful, but awful doesn't last forever.

I'm upset, but I'll live.

I won't lose sleep over this. She'll call me again.

I feel a little unhappy, but I'll be okay.

Have your students pretend they were in Mark's place in the story and told themselves one of the statements above. Ask, "How does it make you feel to tell yourself something kind when you're left out?"

2. Say to your students, "Anytime you're left out, remember there are many more times when you're included. Try to think of those times." Then, help your students make a list of times they have been included. Use these for starters:

when people smile at me when I come in the room

when people sit by me

when people call me

when people invite me places

when people talk to me

when people choose me for teams

when teachers call on me

when family members say nice things to me

3. What kind thing would you say to yourself in these situations?

You raised your hand but the teacher didn't call on you.

The teacher didn't choose you for the play.

Your friend can't play with you tonight.

You sit down in the cafeteria and no one sits by you. You eat all alone.

Skill C

Do Something About It

Ask to Join in

1. Write these tips on the chalkboard or dictate them for your students to write.

Choose a good time. (Discuss good times to join others.)

Decide what to say. (See the activity below.)

Be friendly. (Discuss friendly body language.)

Tell your students there are good and poor ways to try to join in the activities of their friends. Say, "Show thumbs-up for a good way and thumbs-down for a poor way."

You walk up to a group of kids and say:

"Hey, see my new jeans." *down*

"Would you mind if I play, too?" *up*

"Could I go with you guys, too?" *up*

"Here, I'll tell you what to do." *down*

"Let me do that for you." *down*

"Could you use another person? I'd really like to play." *up*

"Would you mind if I try it?" *up*

Ask Why You Were Left Out

1. Point out it's possible to be left out by mistake. Tell your students it's okay to respond to the person who rejected them. For example, a student can feel rejected when a teacher doesn't choose her to answer a question or do a special duty. In that instance, staying after school to talk to the teacher can help the student take positive action for handling hurt feelings. In other instances, a student may want to write to a friend who, for example, didn't invite him to a party or choose her for the team.

2. What would you say to each person who leaves you out in these situations?

    You want to talk to your mom, but she says she has to help your brother with his homework.

    Your grandma has come to visit. You want to go shopping with her, but she says she's taking your sister shopping for her birthday present.

    Brian and Marie were playing a game on the playground and they didn't wait until you got there to start.

Find a New Friend

1. Let students share ways they have made new friends. *being friendly, inviting another person to join an activity, complimenting the person, etc.*

Get into Another Fun Activity

1. Have your students list ideas for things they can do when they feel left out. They might list things like

    take a walk

    dance

    call a friend

    write a letter

    skip rope

    ride a skateboard

    draw a picture

    go down a slide

    practice telling a new joke

Additional Activities

Role-Playing

Review the story in this lesson. Then, select one or more of the following role-play activities.

Choose volunteers to play Mark, José, Bonnie, and Jonathan. Pretend that Mark wasn't invited to go ice skating with the other children. Remind the person playing Mark to use the skills for when he's left out.

Choose volunteers to play Lucy and Lucy's mom. Pretend that Lucy's mom had to feed Lucy's baby sister and change the baby's diapers and didn't have time to read Lucy's favorite book to her. Have the student playing Lucy do something fun to make her feel better.

Choose volunteers to play Fernando and Phil. Pretend that Fernando tells Phil that he doesn't want to be his friend anymore. Remind the student playing Phil to use the skills for when he's left out.

Role-Play Feedback

Encourage the rest of your students to give helpful feedback to the role-play volunteers. Use the following questions:

What did you like about each character's part?

What skills did Mark use when he felt left out?

What skills did Lucy use when she felt left out?

What skills did Phil use when he felt left out?

How could these role plays be different?

Expanding Learning

Use pages 92 through 94 in the Activities Book to help your students

- choose ways to handle hurt feelings
- use helpful self-talk
- choose effective ways to join a group

Use pages 214 through 221 in the Picture Book to help your students discuss and practice social skills they'll need when they experience rejection.

Use page 95 in the Activities Book to help your students review the skills for when they're left out. Have your students suggest when and how they can practice these skills. For example, they might say

"I feel sad because the teacher didn't call on me."

"I will feel better."

"I will ask my teacher why she doesn't call on me."

Visualization

Have your students get in comfortable positions to relax. Then say, "Close your eyes and imagine how well you handled yourself when you were left out.

"You invite your best friend to your house on Saturday. You're excited because you have a new game and you know you'll have a great time together. Your friend says, 'I can't come to your house because I'm spending the day with Taylor.' You feel very disappointed at first. You remember to tell yourself something kind, so you say to yourself, 'This isn't the end of the world. There are other people I can play with. Besides, we'll play together again.'

"You say out loud, 'That's okay. Maybe you can come over some other time.' Then, you think of another friend to invite. You're glad you know what to do when you feel left out."

Lesson 3: Being a Good Sport

Skills

A. Ask yourself, "How well did I play?"

B. If you lose, congratulate the winner.

C. If you win, say "Good game!"

Materials

Activities Book:
pages 96 through 99

Picture Book:
pages 222 through 229

Introduction

Good sportsmanship is an important part of responsible behavior. Winning and losing are daily occurrences in everyone's life.

Some students have a difficult time losing. At their worst, these students cry, pout, or throw tantrums when they lose. Other students brag and gloat when they win. Cheating, not playing by the rules, and blaming losses on teammates are other examples of poor sportsmanship.

Competition through games and sports provides excellent opportunities to develop social language. Games are times for smiling and laughing, greeting others, joining ongoing activities, and extending invitations. Games also provide times for having conversations, sharing, cooperating, and encouraging and complimenting others. Social communication is basic to good sportsmanship.

Goals

In this lesson, your students will have opportunities to improve important social skills related to competitions and contests. The activities will help your students learn to

- evaluate how well they played
- congratulate the winner
- help the loser feel better about not winning

Preparation

How can you help your students communicate graciously whether they win or lose? First, help them enjoy the game. Emphasize the rewards inherent in playing the game, like increased skill, fun, excitement, cooperation, togetherness, physical activity, and feelings of accomplishment. Ask your students to evaluate their activities with these questions:

Who had fun today?

Who played better today than yesterday?

Who caught the ball better? Ran faster?

Who learned a new skill?

Who was a better sport?

Ask, "What does the word *competition* mean?" Explain that when there is competition each person tries to do something better than the others. Games and sports are examples of competition. In sports, there are generally two teams. Each team tries to do better than the other.

Say, "During games and sports there'll be people who are good sports and people who are bad sports. What do good sports do? *Good sports are people who play in such a way that they feel good about themselves whether they win or lose.*

Then, discuss feelings about winning and losing with these questions:

When your team wins, how do you want the losers to act?

When your team loses, how do you want the winners to act?

Social Skills Story

Use page 222 in the Picture Book with this story. Ask your students, "Why is it important to be a good sport instead of a bad sport?" Then say "One day Bonnie saw how a bad sport can spoil all the fun. Listen to this story."

Bonnie and her dad were at Jamal's baseball game to cheer Jamal on.

"Str-r-r-ike one!" shouted the umpire at Jamal's first swing.

"Oh, I hope Jamal hits the next one, Dad," said Bonnie.

The pitcher threw the ball. Jamal swung his bat, but he missed again.

Bonnie yelled, "That's okay! Jamal, you can do it!"

Jamal hit the third ball, but it rolled outside the baseline.

The umpire yelled, "Foul ball!"

A tall girl with brown braids yelled, "Get some glasses, umpire!"

Then, Jamal hit the next ball, and sped toward first base.

"You had a great hit, Jamal!" yelled Bonnie.

When the next player struck out, the girl with brown braids stood up and yelled, "Make him sit on the bench, coach!"

Then, Jamal's team scored two runs. "Way to go!" yelled Bonnie.

When the game was over, Jamal's team lost by one run. Bonnie looked sad, but when the winners walked by, she said, "Good game, boys."

The girl in brown braids said, "Those umpires stink, we'd better get new ones!"

Jamal said to a player on the other team, "You played a good game. I can't wait till we play you again."

Questions for Discussion

Say, "Good sports seem to have fun, even when they lose. Let's talk about the story now and try to think of skills followed by good sports." Write the skills on the chalkboard or a flip chart as your students respond.

1. Who was a bad sport in this story? What are some of the things the bad sport did?

   The girl in the brown braids. She blamed losing on the umpire, yelled "Sit on the bench" to her own player, and complained when her team lost.

2. Who showed they were good sports? What did they do?

   Bonnie and Jamal. Bonnie cheered and Jamal congratulated the winners.

3. Why is it important to try your best for your team?

   Answers will vary.

4. Why is it important to ask yourself after the game, "How well did I play?"

   You'll improve your skills each time you play if you stop and think about what you did well and how you could improve. (Write **Ask yourself, "How well did I play?"***)*

5. If you lose the game, what can you do to be a good sport?

   Shake the winner's hand or say something nice. (Write **If you lose, congratulate the winner.***)*

6. If you win the game, what can you do to be a good sport?

   Don't laugh at the loser. Instead, say something nice to the loser to let him know he played a good game. Don't brag too much or gloat about winning.

7. Pretend you're the loser telling the winner, "Congratulations. You did a good job." Say it sincerely.

   Students will demonstrate. (Write **If you win, say "Good game!"***)*

8. Pretend you're the winner telling the loser something nice, such as "Good game! You were hard to beat."

   Students will demonstrate.

9. Which is more important, to win or to play your best? Why?

   Answers will vary.

Social Skills Activities

Skill A

Ask Yourself, "How Well Did I Play?"

1. Motivate your students to try their best and to be better than the last time they played a game. Have them ask themselves questions specific to the game. Use these questions as guides:

   Did I answer more questions?

   Did I run faster?

   Did I kick the ball farther?

   Did I catch the ball better?

   Did I cheer for my team members?

   Did I cooperate with my teammates?

   Did I listen better?

Ask, "Are you a loser if you answer yes to these questions? Why?"

2. Videotape sports events and watch them in class. Ask, "What made the players seem like good sports? What else could the winners or losers have said or done?"

3. Ask your students to dictate a list of actions they see in people who are good sports. Write them on the chalkboard. Your students might use negative phrasing. For example, they might say: "Don't cheat." "Don't get mad." "Don't yell at your friends." "Don't break the rules." "Don't quit." Accept all their ideas. Then, help them turn the negative phrases into positive phrases. For example, "Don't cheat" would become "Play fair."

Skill B

If You Lose, Congratulate the Winner

1. Use discussion of this skill as an opportunity to build vocabulary and practice nonverbal communication through body language and tone of voice. Ask these discussion questions:

   What does it mean to congratulate someone?

   Is it easy or hard to congratulate the winner?

   If you're the loser, why would you want to congratulate the winner?

2. Point out that the way you act when you lose can show whether you're a good sport or a bad sport. You might want to role-play the statements below for practice identifying good and bad sport behaviors.

   I'll throw a tantrum! *bad*

   You guys make me want to cry! *bad*

   If you hadn't dropped the ball, we would have won. *bad*

   Good game, guys! *good*

   You were a tough team. I can't wait until the next game. *good*

   It was the umpire's fault! *bad*

3. Talk about ways your students can handle their disappointment when they lose. Ask them what they can do to keep from being bad sports. Then, discuss this idea:

   Someone has to lose. If you're the loser, tell yourself, "Someone has to lose. It's okay that I didn't win."

   Suggest that bad sports take games a little too seriously. They think that if they lose a contest, it's the end of the world. Perhaps they picture losers as creeps or geeks. Bad sports can't stand to think of themselves as losers, so they throw tantrums, use bad words, or call the winners names. Ask your students how such behavior makes them look to other people.

4. Say, "I'll tell you some ways bad sports act. Then, you tell me what a good sport might say."

   A bad sport tells a teammate, "We lost because you dropped the ball."

   A bad sport yells to the umpire, "Get some glasses. Can't you see that was a good play?"

   A bad sport tells the losers, "Ha, ha, you lost!"

   A bad sport blames losing on the referee, "We would have won if the referee had been on our side."

   A bad sport says, "I'll go home if you won't play my way."

   When a bad sport starts to lose she says, "I give up. We can't win anyway."

Skill C

If You Win, Say "Good Game!"

1. Have your students pretend they're on the losing team. Ask, "How would you want the winners to act?"

2. Point out the way you act when you win can show whether you're a good winner or a show-off winner. Ask who would act in these ways, a good winner or a show-off winner:

   Say, "You had some great throws. I had a hard time beating you." *good*

   Say, "Ha, ha, ha, you lost!" *show-off*

   Say, "I kicked that ball so far. I was so good. I can't believe how well I played today !" *show-off*

   Say, "Your team did a great job. It was a good match." *good*

   Say, "You put up a good fight. It was a good game." *good*

   You might want to role-play the good winner statements for more practice. Emphasize a sincere tone of voice and positive body language. Ask volunteers to think of other things the winners can say.

Additional Activities

Role-Playing

Review the story in this lesson. Then, select one or both of the following role-play activities.

Choose volunteers to play Jamal and the girl with the brown braids. Pretend that Jamal struck out, but the girl was a good sport. Remind the student playing the girl to use the skills for being a good sport.

Choose volunteers to play Kelly and Julie. Pretend that the girls were playing a board game and Julie won. Pretend Kelly was upset that she didn't win, but she remembered to be a good sport. Remind the student playing Kelly to congratulate Julie.

Role-Play Feedback

Encourage the rest of your students to give positive feedback to the role-play volunteers. Use the following questions:

What did you like about each character's part?

What good sportsmanship skills did the girl with the brown braids use?

What good sportsmanship skills did Kelly use?

How could these role plays be different?

Expanding Learning

Use pages 96 through 98 in the Activities Book to help your students

- practice evaluating how well they play
- practice good sportsmanship in winning and losing while playing a game
- practice what a good sport would say

Use pages 222 through 229 in the Picture Book to help your students communicate good sportsmanship.

Use page 99 in the Activities Book to help your students review the skills for being a good sport. Have your students suggest when and how they can practice these skills. For example, they may say

- "I kicked the ball farther than I did yesterday."

- "You guys did a great job."
- "I had a lot of fun playing with you."

Visualization

Have your students get in comfortable positions to relax. Then say, "Close your eyes and imagine yourself being a good winner.

"You want to be in a class contest. You see yourself practicing very hard. You're chosen for the team.

"Your team wins first place. The principal gives your team a big, silver trophy that says you're the best. You feel very proud of yourself. The principal shakes your hand. Then, you shake the hands of the other students who were in the contest, too. You feel glad you won, but you feel a little bad for the ones who lost. The contest made you work hard to be your best. You feel good about yourself.

"Now, pretend you didn't win the contest. You tried your very best, but some other team won first place. You watch that team win the trophy. After it's over, you go to the winners and congratulate them. You say, 'It was a good contest.' When you leave, you tell yourself you did your best. You try to think of other things you can do so you won't feel too disappointed. The contest made you work hard to be your best. You feel good about yourself. You're glad that you're a good sport."

Lesson 4: Accepting No for an Answer

Skills

A. Why did the person tell you no?

B. Say okay in a friendly way.

C. If you're angry, handle your feelings.

Stay calm.

Tell someone what is bothering you.

Accept a substitute.

Change your mind and do something else.

Materials

Activities Book:
pages 100 through 103

Picture Book:
pages 230 through 237

Introduction

Everyone must learn to accept no from people in charge. No is often given in the form of rules made by parents, teachers, or other adults to protect your students' personal safety. Your students must learn to accept no from peers who turn down invitations or other proposals.

It's helpful to most students to understand that everyone, even adults, must accept no sometimes. Your students need to understand reasons authorities say no, learn to accept no graciously, and accept consequences when they don't accept no.

It's important, however, for your students to handle their frustration when they don't get or can't do what they want. In some instances, they need to know how to complain. In other instances, they need to settle for a substitute. For example, your students can learn to see the value of having a hamster when parents say no to the request for a dog. Students who can accept the word *no* graciously will get along better with those who make rules.

Goals

In this lesson, your students will practice accepting the word *no*. The activities will help your students

- accept the word *no* graciously from authorities and peers
- think about who's saying no—a person in charge or a peer
- consider reasons the other person is saying no
- accept the word *no* and go on to other activities
- accept a substitute
- talk to the other person if the word *no* seems unfair

Preparation

Everyone knows a child who can't take no for an answer. He pouts, cries, begs, whines, or fusses. She talks back, makes faces, tries to get even, or does it anyway. This habit is annoying in a young student and a serious problem in an adolescent.

Even social nos are difficult to accept. There are nos to invitations to play or participate. After all, no one likes to be turned down. Your students will think better of themselves if they learn to accept it when someone says no. Help them remember that if they have the right to say no, so does the other person.

Tell your students about some signs you have seen on your way to work that say no, like "No Smoking" at the gas pump and "No Parking" near the hospital entrance. Ask why it's important to obey those signs. Then, ask your students to tell about signs where they have seen the word *no*. Talk about why such signs are necessary. Talk about reasons teachers and parents say no, like to protect students' health and safety.

Social Skills Story

Use page 230 in the Picture Book with this story. Say, "Think about a time someone said no to you. Was it for a good reason? Was it easy or hard to accept no for an answer?" Then say, "Jonathan wanted something very badly, but he learned to take no for an answer. Listen to this story."

"Dad, can I have a dog?" asked Jonathan.

"I wish you could, Jonathan, but there's no way," Jonathan's dad said.

"You just don't know how badly I want one, Dad!" Jonathan argued.

Jonathan's mom said, "We don't have any room for a dog in this small apartment, Jonathan. And it's also against the apartment rules."

Jonathan sighed and said, "I can't help it. I just wish I had a dog."

"Why does the apartment have a rule like that? I would take care of my dog. I wouldn't let him bother anyone. I would keep him on a leash when I took him outside." Jonathan seemed to have all the reasons it would be okay for him to have a dog.

Dad said, "What about when you're at school and Mom and I are at work? A dog would get tired of staying inside all day by itself."

Jonathan sighed, "Yeah, I guess so."

That night, Jonathan dreamed that he had a dog. When he woke up, he jumped out of bed to see his dog. Then, he remembered it was only a dream. He wanted to cry. Jonathan had tried to accept no for an answer, but his disappointment made it hard.

Dad said, "Jonathan, your mom and I know how hard you're trying to accept no for an answer. How would you feel about getting a cat instead? A cat could be a substitute for a dog. Cats are allowed in our apartment."

Jonathan said, "A dog would be more fun, but, a cat could be fun, too."

Jonathan didn't feel disappointed anymore. He understood that he couldn't have a dog. Now he's happy with the substitute, his cat Marlowe.

Questions for Discussion

Say, "Now, let's talk about the story and list the skills for accepting no for an answer." Write the skills on the chalkboard or a flip chart as your students respond.

1. Why did Mom and Dad tell Jonathan no?

   Dogs weren't allowed in their apartment; the apartment was too small; no one was home to let the dog out during the day. (Write **Why did the person tell you no?***)*

2. Was there any way Jonathan's mom and dad could say yes? Why?

   No. It was against the rules.

3. Even adults have to accept no for an answer. What are some other nos adults must accept?

   Answers will vary.

4. True or false. When the answer is absolutely no, it's best to say okay.

   true (Write **Say okay in a friendly way.***)*

5. Jonathan tried to accept no for an answer, but he felt very disappointed. Why?

   He wanted a dog.

6. Jonathan's mom and dad were able to help Jonathan handle his feelings. Explain.

   They said they would let him have a cat as a substitute for the dog he wanted. (Write **If you're angry, handle your feelings. Accept a substitute.***)*

7. How else can we handle our feelings of disappointment or anger?

   Answers will vary. (Write **Tell someone what is bothering you.***)*

8. It's important to stay calm when you accept no. Why?

   so the other person won't get angry (Write **Stay calm.***)*

9. Pretend the apartment owner's rule said, No Pets Allowed. That includes dogs, cats, gerbils, hamsters, and fish. What are some fun activities Jonathan could do besides having a pet?

   Answers will vary. (Write **Change your mind and do something else.***)*

10. What's wrong with these responses to no: Pouting? Whining? Crying? Fussing? Arguing? Talking back? Making faces? Doing it anyway?

    Answers will vary.

Social Skills Activities

Skill A

Why Did the Person Tell You No?

1. Talk about different people who might tell your students no and reasons they might say no. Distinguish between authorities and peers.

   Authorities: Ask your students, "Who are some people you should obey? These are usually people who are in charge." *parents, teachers, principals, baby-sitters, camp counselors, etc.*

   Point out that even adults must accept no for an answer sometimes. Ask your students to list some people their parents must accept no from. *employers, business associates, judges; answers will vary*

   Peers: Ask, "Do friends sometimes tell you no? When? How do you feel when you hear a friend say no?" *Friends may say no when you ask them to come to a party, to come out to play, or to lend you some of their toys; answers will vary.*

2. Discuss reasons people in charge and even friends say no. Write these reasons on the chalkboard or on sentence strips:

   It's too dangerous.

   It's a bad time.

   We can't afford it.

   It would bother someone else.

   It would hurt someone else.

   It's against the law.

   Say, "Pretend you're the person in charge. I'll ask you for something. Then, you tell me no in a friendly way, and tell me one of these reasons above." Call on students randomly:

   You're my mother. I'd like to buy some new tennis shoes.

   You're the teacher. I need a drink of water during a test.

   You're the bus driver. I want to stand up on the bus.

   You're my father. I want to go bungee jumping.

   You're the baby-sitter. I want a candy bar.

   You're the judge. I want to drive faster than the speed limit.

Skill B

Say Okay in a Friendly Way

1. First, have your students name rules for the school and classroom. List them on the chalkboard. Write the rules in the negative:

   No running in the hall
   No talking in the library
   No hitting; No yelling
   Don't throw things
   Don't use other people's things
   Don't break things

   Then say, "Pretend I'm a student and you're the teacher in charge. You saw me break one of the rules. I'm not going to answer in a friendly way. You show me a better way to behave." Ask your students to explain the consequences of each poor behavior listed below.

   I'm running in the hall. You say, "You may not run in the hall." (Respond by whining.)

   I'm breaking someone's pencil. You say, "You may not break someone's pencil." (Respond by pouting.)

   I'm throwing food in the lunch room. You say, "You may not throw food." (Respond by begging.)

   I'm yelling in the hallway. You say, "You may not yell at school." (Respond by making a face behind the teacher's back.)

2. Read *The Tale of Peter Rabbit*, the classic tale of the little rabbit who disobeyed his mother, went to Mr. MacGregor's garden, and almost wound up in Mrs. MacGregor's rabbit pie. Then, ask your students these questions:

   Before she left, what did Mrs. Rabbit tell Peter, Flopsy, Mopsy, and Cottontail to do?

   What did Flopsy, Mopsy, and Cottontail do? What did Peter do?

   What happened to Peter in the garden?

   How did Peter get away?

   What happened to Peter's clothes?

   Why did Peter and the other rabbits have different things for supper?

   Next, have your students change the story and have Peter obey his mother. Then, retell the story.

Help your students name other things Peter could have done besides get into Mr. MacGregor's garden.

Skill C

If You're Angry, Handle Your Feelings

Stay Calm

1. Explain to your students that it's best to stay calm when they begin to feel angry, want to talk back, or act out angry feelings. Remind them of ways to calm down, such as counting to ten slowly, taking three deep breaths, or walking away for a few seconds. For other ideas for calming down, see the Appendix.

Tell Someone What Is Bothering You

1. Refer to the story in this lesson and ask:

   Who did Jonathan talk to about his feelings of frustration?

   Who are some people you can talk to about your feelings?

   Why does it help to talk to someone about your upset feelings?

2. Talk to the person who said no. Point out that there are times when no is unfair. At such times, it's okay to complain. Remember to use "I-messages." Begin your statements with words like "I feel . . . ," "I wish . . . ," and "I want . . . ."

   Here are some unfair situations to use for practice.

   You ask your sister to talk on the phone in another room so you can watch TV in a quiet room. She says no. *I feel angry when you won't listen to me. I want to be able to hear the TV.*

   You share a locker or cubbie with your friend who is taking up most of the space with her things. You asked her to move her things so you'll have more room, but she said no. *I'm upset when you won't move your things. I need more space.*

   You ask the storekeeper to take back a toy that was broken when you bought it, but he said no. *I feel that it's not fair that I should pay for a toy that's broken, and I want my money back.*

Accept a Substitute

1. List substitutes for the situations below:

   You want a new game, but your mom doesn't have enough money for it.

   You want to sleep with your old teddy bear, but it has been thrown out.

   You want to wear your favorite shirt, but it's in the wash.

   Your mom wants to use the dishwasher, but it's broken.

   Your dad wants to take a vacation, but the boss won't let him because things are too busy at work.

Change Your Mind and Do Something Else

1. Sometimes it's best to change your mind about what you want, especially in situations that just won't change. Tell the following story.

   When Marci first moved to her new house, she was very unhappy because she missed her old school, old friends, and old teachers. She complained to her mother that she was angry about having to move away from the town she loved. She begged to move back. Her mom said, "No, we can't move back to our old home. I don't have a job in that town anymore. We have to stay here." No matter how much Marci cried or yelled, they couldn't move back.

After a while, Marci realized there was nothing she could do. She had to stay in the new town. Finally, she stopped wishing she could move back to her old town.

Then, something good began happening. When she stopped wishing for something she couldn't have, she started feeling better. Instead of crying and feeling sad, she started acting friendly to other kids. Soon, she substituted many new friends for old ones in her school and neighborhood. Marci felt happy again.

Use these questions for discussion.

How did Marci feel when she moved to her new town?

What did Marci change her mind about?

Why do you think Marci started feeling happy again?

Additional Activities

Role-Playing

Review the story in this lesson. Then, select one or more of the following role-play activities.

Choose volunteers to play Jonathan and his dad. Pretend that Jonathan accepts no for an answer when his dad tells him he can't have a dog or any other animal. Remind the student playing Jonathan to use the skills for accepting no for an answer.

Choose volunteers to play Damien and his mom and dad. Pretend Damien's parents think Damien is hanging around a bad group of kids. Damien's parents won't let Damien play with them. Remind the student playing Damien to use the skills for accepting no for an answer.

Choose volunteers to play Mark and Mark's doctor. Pretend Mark broke his leg and he's tired of wearing his cast. Mark asks the doctor to take the cast off and the doctor says, "No, your leg isn't healed yet." Remind the student playing Mark to use the skills for accepting no for an answer.

Role-Play Feedback

Encourage the rest of your students to give helpful feedback to role-play volunteers.

Use the following questions:

What did you like about each character's part?

What skills for accepting no for an answer did Jonathan use?

What skills for accepting no for an answer did Damien use?

What skills for accepting no for an answer did Mark use?

How could these role plays be different?

Expanding Learning

Use pages 100 through 102 in the Activities Book to help your students

- recognize and describe poor ways to accept no for an answer
- deal with taking no for an answer by listing other activities they can do
- understand limitations that everyone must follow

Use pages 230 through 237 in the Picture Book to help your students accept no.

Use page 103 in the Activities Book to help your students review the skills for accepting no for an answer. Have your students suggest when and how they'll practice these skills. For example, they might say

> "I was told no because my mom thought roller blading was dangerous."
>
> "Okay, I won't roller-blade."
>
> "I will roller-skate instead."

Visualization

Have your students get in comfortable positions to relax. Then say, "Close your eyes and imagine yourself accepting no for an answer in a friendly way.

"Your parents tell you no when you ask to go to a swimming party because you can't swim. You understand the reason they said no. They think it's too dangerous. They would worry about you. You really think you'd be okay, but you don't argue. You don't beg or talk back. You don't whine or cry. Instead, you say 'Okay.'

"Then, you try to think of something else you can do that you'll enjoy. You ask your parents if you can have a friend who's not going to the party come over to play. They say yes. You and your friend have a good time together. You're glad you know how to accept no for an answer, handle your feelings, and find other fun activities to do."

Lesson 5: Saying No

Skills

A. Ask yourself, "Do I want to do this?"

B. Say no kindly.

C. Give a reason, if you can.

Materials

Activities Book:
pages 104 through 107

Picture Book:
pages 238 through 245

Introduction

How your students use the words *yes* and *no* is important. They're faced daily by others who make requests and place demands. The simple word *no* helps them control their lives. Everyone must say no to some activities if he is to say yes to the ones he values more.

Your students need to say no firmly when saying yes would cause them to get in trouble, become embarrassed, hurt someone else, go against a personal value, or violate their own wants and wishes. They must consider consequences of such actions as taking drugs, smoking cigarettes, stealing, cheating, and teasing. Mumbling and grumbling and going along anyway are ineffective choices that don't show respect for others. A simple no would be kinder.

It's important for your students to know how to say no kindly. Often people feel guilty saying no, so they say it unpleasantly and hurt others' feelings. Your students will learn they can smile when they say no.

Goals

This lesson will help teach your students how to say no responsibly. The activities will help your students

- discuss when it's appropriate to say no
- practice saying no firmly
- practice saying no kindly

Preparation

The word *no* brings to mind negative associations, like rejection, failure, weakness, selfishness, risking anger, and hurting the feelings of others. But saying no is also associated with honesty, authority, power, confidence, integrity, and freedom from being used.

Have your students write the word *no* on a sheet of paper and draw a situation in which they would say no. Ask your students to share their drawings with the class. Then, sort their various situations into the following four groups:

- saying no to stay out of dangerous situations
- saying no because you prefer to use your time in a different way
- saying no to keep from hurting someone
- saying no to be honest

Social Skills Story

Use page 238 in the Picture Book with this story. Focus on the importance of thinking about the consequences when someone asks you to participate in an activity. Say, "Saying no takes courage. One day Marci needed courage to say no when she least expected it. Listen to this story."

Marci was taking a bus by herself to visit her cousin Sandra and her Aunt Barb. Sandra was only two years older than Marci, but Sandra acted even older.

When Marci jumped off the bus with her suitcase, Sandra ran to meet her. "I'll carry your suitcase, Marci. Mom's waiting in the car. Let's go!"

Marci walked with Sandra toward the back entrance of the station where Aunt Barb was waiting. Suddenly, Sandra set the suitcase down and pulled a package of cigarettes from her pocket. Sandra said, "Look, Marci, when we get home, we'll go out back and try some of these. I'll teach you how to smoke."

Marci felt uncomfortable. "Let's go see Aunt Barb," she said.

When Marci saw her aunt, she gave her a hug.

In the car, Marci had trouble listening to Aunt Barb tell about the things she had planned for Marci and Sandra to do during the week. She kept thinking about the cigarettes.

First, Marci thought, "I don't want Sandra to think I'm a baby. But, cigarettes are unhealthy. You can get cancer and other diseases if you smoke them." Then, Marci thought about what her Aunt Barb would say if she caught the girls smoking. "She would call Mom," thought Marci. "Then, I'd get grounded!" Marci made up her mind that she wouldn't smoke the cigarettes.

Later, Marci stood as tall as she could, looked at Sandra, and said, "Hey, cigarette smoking is not for me. I won't be smoking with you."

Sandra tried to get Marci to change her mind, but Marci told her that she didn't want to get the diseases that cigarettes cause. "Besides," Marci said, "I don't want to get in trouble."

Questions for Discussion

Say, "It was tough for Marci, but she had the courage to say no. Let's talk about the story and think of skills that anyone could follow to say no." Write the skills on the chalkboard or a flip chart as your students respond.

1. What did Marci's cousin want her to do?

    smoke cigarettes with her

2. Do you think Marci asked herself whether or not she wanted to go along with her cousin and smoke the cigarettes? How could you tell?

    Yes. She thought about what would happen if she smoked. She thought about reasons for not smoking. (Write **Ask yourself, "Do I want to do this?"***)*

3. Why did Marci think she should smoke?

    so her cousin wouldn't think she was a baby

4. If Marci had joined her cousin in smoking, she wouldn't have to feel bad about being different. Do you think that's a good reason for doing something you don't want to do? Why?

    No. Going along with others' wishes can get you in trouble; it's okay to say no; answers will vary.

5. What were some of the consequences of smoking cigarettes that Marci thought about?

    getting diseases from cigarettes, being punished

6. Why is it important to think about the consequences of what you do?

    It can keep you from hurting yourself or someone else.

7. Did Marci tell her cousin no in a mean, angry way or in a kind way?

    a kind way (Write **Say no kindly.***)*

8. What could happen if you shout, yell, or put the other person down when you say no?

    She might get angry; answers will vary.

9. Sometimes, saying no isn't enough. Sometimes, you need to explain why. What did Marci say to explain why she didn't want to smoke cigarettes?

    She told her cousin she didn't want to get diseases that are caused by cigarettes and she didn't want to get in trouble. (Write **Give a reason, if you can.***)*

10. Marci felt better about herself after she told her cousin no, even though her cousin might have been angry with her. Why?

    She stood up for herself; she did what she thought was best.

Social Skills Activities

Skill A

Ask Yourself, "Do I Want to Do This?"

1. Discuss when it's appropriate to say no. Say, "There are many activities you might need to say no to. Can you think of some?"

Use the following list to guide your discussion:

Activities you're not allowed to do, like going out at night alone, cooking on the stove without an adult helping, and cutting the grass.

Activities that might get you in trouble, like stealing, lying, cheating, and destroying property.

Activities that are dangerous or might hurt someone, like taking drugs or alcohol, smoking, fighting, and laughing at someone.

Activities you don't enjoy, like watching a football game, playing soccer, and other personal preferences.

Activities you do enjoy, but can't do because you have other plans, like being invited to a movie when you have to go to the dentist.

2. Discuss the consequences of certain actions. Thinking of the consequences can help your students say no when necessary. Ask, "What are the consequences of robbing a bank? Do you think a bank robber thinks seriously about going to jail before robbing a bank?" Then, discuss the consequences of these actions:

   taking drugs

   smoking cigarettes

   stealing from someone

   cheating at school

   joining in teasing others

   doing a fun activity when you've promised to do some work

   Explain to your students that saying no to dangerous activities, like taking drugs, says they like themselves enough to want to take care of their lives, not destroy them.

Skill B

Say No Kindly

1. Point out that people often feel guilty about saying no, especially to invitations that they can't accept because they have other plans. If they say no unpleasantly, they might hurt others' feelings.

   Help your students see that they don't have to frown or look away when they say no.

   Instead, your students can look at the person and smile. Adding words like "Thank you" adds kindness to their no. Tell them these examples: "That's nice of you to ask me, but no thanks." "Thanks for asking, but I've made other plans. Perhaps another time." Have your students practice saying no kindly with the following situations:

   A friend asks you to a party, but you're going to your grandma's.

   A friend asks you to go swimming with his family, but you're afraid to swim.

   A friend asks you to go on a bike ride, but your bike is broken.

   Your teacher asks you if you want to stay after school with some other students to help plan an activity, but you have a doctor's appointment.

2. Practice saying the following answers kindly, and firmly:

   "No. That's not for me."

   "I can't because I have to visit my grandma."

   "No. I'm not allowed to go anywhere on school nights."

   "No. It makes me feel bad when I do that."

   "No. Mom and Dad won't let me."

   "I know you like to eat pickles and ice cream, but I don't want to."

   "Hey, I don't do that stuff."

   "No thank you. I don't care for that TV show."

3. Say, "I'll tell you some angry ways to say no. Then, you think of a nicer way to say no."

   Request: "Why don't you buy a shirt like mine?"
   Answer: "That's stupid."

   Request: "Would you like to watch my Bambi video?"
   Answer: "Are you kidding? Nobody cares about that tape anymore!"

   Request: "Do you want to share my Cracker Jacks?"
   Answer: "Don't you ever remember that I'm allergic to peanuts?"

Skill C

Give a Reason, if You Can

1. Point out that sometimes saying no isn't enough, so it's a good idea to give a reason.

   First, help your students sort out reasons they might want to say no. List these reasons on the chalkboard:

   It's dangerous.

   I'm not allowed.

   I have other plans.

   It makes me feel bad.

   It might hurt someone.

   I'd rather not.

   I might get in trouble.

   Point out that there may be more than one reason for saying no to some activities. Have your students sort the following activities into these reasons for saying no:

   Another student wants to cut in front of you in line.

   Your brother wants to watch another TV program before the show you're watching is over. He changes the TV channel.

   Some kids want you to join in teasing a new student at school.

   Another student wants you to throw a spitball in class.

   Someone dares you to say something cruel to a student who is handicapped.

   A friend wants to come in and play, but your parents told you not to have anyone in while they're gone.

   A friend asks you to get in the car and you know the driver has been drinking.

   You're invited to a birthday party, but you promised your grandmother you would help her dust her apartment.

   Your sister wants to borrow your new tape, but you know she doesn't take care of her own tapes.

2. Use the puppets on page 105 in the Activities Book to role-play the situations and answers above.

Additional Activities

Role-Playing

Review the story in this lesson. Then, select one or more of the following role-play activities.

Choose volunteers to play Marci and her cousin Sandra. Pretend Sandra asks Marci if she wants to smoke cigarettes. Marci says no. Remind the student playing Marci to use the skills for saying no.

Choose volunteers to play Rockey and Rob. Pretend Rockey asks Rob to go roller skating, but Rob doesn't like to roller skate. Remind the student playing Rob to say no kindly.

Choose volunteers to play Jackie and Lynette. Pretend Lynette asked Jackie over to play some video games, but Jackie said she couldn't because she was going to visit her aunt. Remind the student playing Jackie to tell why she can't come over.

Role-Play Feedback

Encourage the rest of your students to give helpful feedback to the role-play volunteers. Use the following questions:

What did you like about each character's part?

What skills did Marci use for telling Sandra no?

What skills did Rob use for telling Rockey no?

What skills did Jackie use to tell Lynette no?

How could these role plays be different?

Expanding Learning

Use pages 104 through 106 in the Activities Book to help your students

- say no kindly when they have different plans
- role-play with puppets
- say a definite no when they need to refuse to do something that would harm someone

Use pages 238 through 245 in the Picture Book to help your students say no.

Use page 107 in the Activities Book to help your students review the skills for saying no. Have your students suggest when and how they'll practice the skills for saying no. For example, they may say

"Do I want to tease Hans?"

"I will tell Joe nicely, 'I don't want to tease Hans.' "

"I think teasing hurts people's feelings."

Visualization

Have your students get in comfortable positions to relax. Then say, "Close your eyes and imagine yourself saying no.

"Your friend has bought some expensive tennis shoes and wants you to buy some just like his. You know your parents don't want you to have those expensive shoes. You smile and say in a kind way, 'I think your shoes are great, but my parents won't let me have them. Thanks anyway!'

"Your friend understands and smiles at you, too. Then, you both decide to ride your skateboards and have a good time together. You're glad you know how to say no in a way that doesn't hurt someone."

Lesson 6: Handling Disagreements

Skills

A. What does each person need?

B. Think of all your choices.

C. Look at the consequences.

D. Make the best choice.

E. Make a plan.

F. Ask yourself, "How did it work?"

Materials

Activities Book:
pages 108 through 110

Picture Book:
pages 246 through 253

Introduction

All students get into quarrels and fights. Those disagreeing need to find solutions for their problems that are acceptable to everyone.

This type of problem solving has been called a "win-win" method for resolving conflict. In such an approach, no one loses. People who disagree communicate responsibly.

This method for conflict resolution has potential to strengthen relationships. It will help your students work together to find mutually acceptable solutions to their conflicts. The focus is on making choices to meet personal needs. Such problem solving becomes a responsible, friendship-strengthening process.

Goals

In this lesson, your students will learn to problem solve in order to handle disagreements. The activities will help your students

- identify the problem
- think of solutions
- carry out the solutions

Preparation

Help your students think about their conflicts as problem-solving opportunities. Then, help your students learn to ask, "Do you have any ideas how we could think together to find an answer to this problem so we'll both be happy?"

Explain to your students that when two people don't agree on something, we say they're in *conflict*. It's perfectly normal to disagree with others. No one agrees with everyone all the time. A conflict can be like a puzzle to solve or a problem that needs an answer. A conflict can be a good thing or a bad thing. How we handle conflict determines whether it's good or bad. Then ask your students, "What causes people to have disagreements, fights, or conflicts?"

Social Skills Story

Use page 246 in the Picture Book with this story. Ask, "Is it important for people to settle disagreements without getting mad at each other? Why?" Then say, "Chee and her younger sister, Mia, had a conflict. Listen to this story."

Chee was playing the piano. She suddenly stopped and roared, "Turn that stupid tape player down, Mia! I can't hear what I'm playing."

Mia marched down the hall toward Chee and shouted, "I'm sick of hearing your piano music over and over. I want to drown it out!" Chee had been practicing every day for her piano recital. Mia grew tired of Chee's music. That afternoon, Mia decided to solve her problem. She turned up her tape player so she couldn't hear the piano music.

Mia's answer to her problem, however, created a problem for Chee. Mia's tape bothered Chee so much she couldn't practice.

"Grandmother!" yelled Chee.

Grandmother looked concerned. "Do you girls have a problem?" she asked.

"Yes," explained Mia. "Chee's playing the piano too loudly. I'm sick of hearing her. I can't even hear my tape player."

"Well," Chee interrupted. "I have to practice for my recital, Grandmother. Mia knows that! How can I practice when she plays her music so loud? It's impossible!" Chee frowned at Mia and folded her arms across her chest.

Grandmother said, "It sounds as if both of you need a quiet house for your work and play. See if you can think of some ways to solve the problem that'll make both of you happy."

"Well," said Chee with a grin. "Mia could fly to outer space! My piano wouldn't bother her there." Then, Chee burst into laughter.

"Or maybe I could blow up Chee's piano with dynamite!" said Mia.

Grandmother smiled and said, "Keep thinking. What other solutions could make you both happy?" asked Grandma.

Mia said, "I could get some earphones for my tape player."

"Or maybe," said Chee, "I could practice my piano at school."

Then, Grandmother named all the girls' solutions. She said, "I'll have to cross out the outer space and dynamite ideas. Your other ideas might work. Now, make a plan to try them out."

Questions for Discussion

Say to your students,"Let's talk about the story and list the skills so we can use them to solve our own problems." Write the skills on the chalkboard or a flip chart as your students respond.

1. What were the girls disagreeing about?

   Chee's piano music and Mia's loud tape player

2. The girls had a problem because each of them wanted something she wasn't getting. What did each girl need?

   Chee needed quiet in order to practice her piano; Mia needed a break from hearing the same piano music every day. (Write **What does each person need?***)*

3. True or false? It's okay to think of many different ideas when you're thinking of ways to solve problems.

   true (Write **Think of all your choices.***)*

4. What were the girls' choices?

   sending Mia to outer space, blowing up the piano, getting earphones, practicing at school

5. Could the girls use all of the choices? Why?

   No. Flying into outer space and blowing up the piano wouldn't work. (Write **Look at the consequences.***)*

6. Which solutions did the girls choose?

   buy earphones, practice at school (Write **Make the best choice.***)*

7. Grandmother told Mia and Chee to make a plan after they chose what to do. Why?

   Making a plan would help them get to work on the problem and decide when and where to work on it; answers will vary. (Write **Make a plan.***)*

8. How do you think the plan worked? What could they do if the plan didn't work?

   Answers will vary. (Write **Ask yourself, "How did it work?"***)*

Social Skills Activities

Skill A
What Does Each Person Need?

1. Help your students learn to define problems for themselves. Help them think of a problem in terms of what each person needs. Focus on what your students *see* and *hear*, what they *feel* about the situation, and what they want to *change*. For example, in the story both Chee and Mia needed quiet in order to practice or play. Chee said, "I need to practice the piano."

   Have your students name the problem in each of the following stories in terms of each person. Then, have them practice being the child with the problem and say, "I need . . . ."

   Michelle wanders around on the playground by herself. She wants to play with Stephanie and Cassandra. Every time she goes up to talk to them on the playground, they run away. Then, Michelle yells names at them. What does Michelle need? *Michelle needs friends to play with on the playground.*

   Mom asked Meredith and Jameson where they wanted to go eat supper. Jameson wanted to go to Hamburger Heaven for hamburgers, and Meredith wanted to go to South of the Border for enchiladas. What do Meredith and Jameson need? *They want different foods.*

Jeffrey has enough money to buy some new jeans for Western Day tomorrow. He asks his mom to go to the mall now so he can buy them. Mom wants to finish the laundry and start supper because both of them need to go to a meeting after supper. What do they need? *Jeffrey needs to go shopping; Mom needs to do laundry and start supper.*

Mom brings home a new video game for her three children. Each child reaches for the game. They begin to argue. What's the problem? *Each child wants to play with the video game.*

2. Ask your students,"What are some things people do when they don't agree about something?" Then, explain to them that they need to find answers to solve their problems. Discuss some of the following tips:

   Believe conflict can be solved.

   Don't try to decide who's right and who's wrong.

   Don't allow physical or verbal violence.

   Use I-messages such as "I want . . . " or "I feel . . . ."

   Use active listening. Try to understand the other person.

   If feelings are strong, take time to cool down.

   Choose good times to talk. Also, allow everyone time to talk.

   Ask for what you want. Say, "I want to tell you how I feel about . . . ."

   Be willing to change.

   Stick to the current conflict.

   Forgive others and ask forgiveness.

   Try to laugh at yourself sometimes.

Skill B

Think of All Your Choices

1. Choose one of the problems from Skill A or have your students give a situation in which the problem has been defined. Guide your students in brainstorming choices.

   Say to your students, "Let's see how many choices for solving problems we can come up with." Remember, your students' decision-making abilities are enhanced only if they have at least two choices. In this skill, try for quantity, not quality. Don't allow students to make fun of any ideas. Go for far-out ideas. Help your students learn to ask, "Do we have any ideas about how we could solve this problem so we could both feel okay?" Write the choices on the chalkboard.

Skill C

Look at the Consequences

1. Review each of the choices you wrote during Skill B and cross off the ones that someone doesn't like or that won't work. Cross off the choices you find unacceptable, too. Talk about why the discarded choices won't work. Then, talk about the positive and negative consequences of each choice. Encourage your students to tell each other why they like their ideas.

Skill D

Make the Best Choice

1. Now, choose the best solution. The best solution is the one with the fewest negative consequences and the most positive consequences. Then, ask your students to imagine how each solution they didn't cross off the list would work. Ask, "If you tried this idea, what do you think would happen? Would you solve the problem?" Work toward a consensus among your students.

Skill E
Make a Plan

1. It's not enough to decide what's best to do, you must get to work and do it. For example, say to your students, "Pretend that you share a bedroom with your brother. Your brother makes a mess all over the bedroom all the time. The best choice is to divide the room into two sections, so each of you has your own space.

   "You can do what you want in your own space. Now, put your plan into action." Discuss the following questions:

   What changes need to be made?

   How will you start?

   Who does what?

   How long will this plan last?

   When is your part of the plan done?

   How well must your part of the plan be done?

   When will you evaluate your plan?

   How will you evaluate it?

Skill F
Ask Yourself, "How Did It Work?"

1. Finally, have your students assess the results of dividing the bedroom into two sections. Is the problem solved? Is it better? Worse? The same?

   It's important for your students to understand that plans don't always work. That's okay. Discuss these ideas:

   If what you tried didn't work, try something different.

   You may need to talk with someone.

   You may need some help.

Additional Activities

Role-Playing

Review the story in this lesson. Then, select one or more of the following role-play activities.

Choose volunteers to play Chee and Mia. Pretend that Chee needs to practice the piano for a recital and Mia is sick of hearing the same song over and over. Remind the students playing these roles to use the skills for handling disagreements.

Choose volunteers to play Steve and his brother, Andrew. Pretend the boys argue about who gets the bathroom first in the mornings. Remind the students playing the boys to come up with choices and choose the best ones.

Choose volunteers to be students. Pretend that there is only one computer in your classroom. Your class can't agree on how to get equal chances to use the computer. Remind the students playing in this role play to use the skills for handling disagreements.

Role-Play Feedback

Encourage the rest of the students to give helpful feedback to the role-play volunteers. Use the following questions:

What did you like about each character's part?

What choices for solving their disagreement did Chee and Mia use?

How did Steve and Andrew solve their disagreement?

How did the class solve its problem?

How could these role plays be different?

Expanding Learning

Use pages 108 and 109 in the Activities Book to help your students

- think of alternatives for solving disagreements
- think of people who can help them when they can't work out their disagreements
- evaluate how well a plan for solving a disagreement has worked

Use pages 246 through 253 in the Picture Book to help your students handle disagreements.

Use page 110 in the Activities Book to help your students review the skills for handling disagreements. Have your students suggest when and how they will practice the skills. For example, they might say

"I need you to stop changing the channels with the remote control all the time."

"I could buy my own TV."

"If I buy my own TV, it would cost me more money than I have."

"Let's take turns changing the channels."

"I will change the channels on Monday nights."

"It worked."

Visualization

Have your students get in comfortable positions to relax. Then say, "Close your eyes and imagine yourself disagreeing with your parents.

"Your parents want you to visit your grandma on Sunday afternoons with them. You want to visit your grandma, but you like to ride bikes with kids in your neighborhood on Sunday afternoons. You know your grandma gets lonely and likes to see you. Your parents understand that you like to be with the kids, too, so you and your parents try to think of some choices to solve the problem.

"You come up with three choices: 1) visit your grandma on Saturday one week and Sunday the next week, 2) invite your grandma to spend the weekend at your house, 3) see if you can get the kids to ride bikes on Saturday afternoons instead of Sundays. You decide to try the last choice.

"Your parents agree to try another choice if your choice doesn't work after two weeks. You feel happy because you're learning to solve problems and work out disagreements so that both you and your parents are happy. This way, everyone wins!"

Appendix

Relaxation Techniques

Goal: to learn a variety of relaxation techniques to be used when feelings are hard to control

Procedures

Ask your students, "When you feel upset, someone may say to you, 'Just relax.' Do you know what to do?" Explain that *relax* means to unwind, calm down, or slow down. Relaxing can sometimes be hard to do.

Say to your students, "Relaxing when you're upset takes practice. It's important to learn to calm down when you get upset. That way you can think about what you need to do."

Explain to your students that relaxing won't solve all their problems. Tell them that it's difficult, however, to make good decisions or act the way they want when they're upset. Ideas come more quickly when they're relaxed.

Establish a quiet atmosphere by dimming lights or playing relaxing music. Relate instructions to your students in a calm, gentle voice. Go slowly.

Direct relaxation exercises by having your students get into comfortable positions, like sitting in their chairs or sitting at their desks with their heads down.

Breathing Technique

Begin this exercise while students are seated. Say, "Breathe in and out quickly, as you might do if you were very frightened by a wild animal." (Allow only about 10 quick breaths.)

Ask, "How do you feel? That's the way you feel when you're scared or upset about something. You can learn to take several deep breaths when you begin to feel nervous or scared."

Now, have your students put one hand on their stomachs. Say, "Watch your hand moving as you breathe in and out. Can you feel your hand move?"

Say, "Now breathe in as I count. Breathe in: 1, 2, 3, 4. Hold it: 1, 2. Breathe out: 1, 2, 3, 4. Say the words *calm down* as you breathe out."

Say, "Keep breathing in and out slowly. Pretend your stomach is a big balloon. Let the big balloon push your hand up as you breathe in. Gently push the balloon down as you breathe out."

Ask, "How do you feel? Breathing this way should help you feel relaxed."

Reinforce your students' attempts to breathe in this way. Keep the practice period short. You may need to have several practice sessions.

Then, explain that your students can use this skill whenever they feel tense or upset. You may want to arrange a special signal with some students so you can silently remind them to use their breathing technique.

Muscle Relaxation

Ask, "Has your neck ever felt stiff? When you feel upset or worried, your body tightens up and causes you to feel pain. You can stop your muscles from tightening by using muscle relaxation."

Have your students get in comfortable positions. Next, have your students practice their breathing for a few moments.

Say, "Now, make a fist. Tighten your fist and arm so that you make a muscle. Squeeze very tight and hold it while I count to ten: 1, 2, 3, 4, 5, 6, 7, 8, 9, 10. Now, slowly open your hand and shake it out. Let your hand flop like a giant noodle."

Repeat this exercise with both arms. Try gently lifting and releasing students' arms. Their arms will feel limp and heavy if they're truly relaxed. End the exercise with a few moments of relaxed breathing. On another day, continue with other parts of the body: the muscles in the jaw, feet, calves, thighs, stomach, neck, and face.

Imagination

Explain to your students, "You're using your imagination when you see yourself doing something else or being somewhere else. Your imagination can help you relax. For example, close your eyes and imagine that you are floating in a swimming pool on a big, soft raft. Feel the water making you sway gently on your raft. Feel the warm sun on your body. Feel a gentle, warm breeze on your face. Now, don't you feel yourself calming down and relaxing?"

Say, "When you feel tense or upset, imagine yourself in a relaxing place. When you're doing something you enjoy, you relax."

Explain that these exercises can be used anywhere and anytime.